STEP UP 成长 with CHINESE
for beginners!

WORKBOOK

编委会

特别顾问： Honorary Consultant	崔希亮 **Xiliang Cui**			

顾问： Consultants	刘珣 **Xun Liu**	崔永华 **Yonghua Cui**

北京语言大学 Beijing Language & Culture University:

编者： Writers	陈丽霞 **Lixia Chen**	张兰欣 **Lanxin Zhang**	王枫 **Feng Wang**	徐式婧 **Shijing Xu**
	黄雯雯 **Wenwen Huang**	高小丽 **Xiaoli Gao**	孟艳华 **Yanhua Meng**	

美国教育专家 American Educators:

竹露茜 **Lucy Chu Lee**	陶洁琳 **Janice Dowd**	陈少元 **Carol Chen-Lin**	谭大立 **Dali Tan**	赵丹 **Dan Zhao**

CENGAGE
Learning®

Andover • Melbourne • Mexico City • Stamford, CT • Toronto • Hong Kong • New Delhi • Seoul • Singapore • Tokyo

Step Up with Chinese Workbook

Publishing Director, CLT Product Director:
Paul K. H. Tan

Editorial Manager:
Zhao Lan

Editor:
Titus Teo

Creative Manager:
Melvin Chong

Product Manager (Outside Asia):
Mei Yun Loh

Development Editor:
Coco Koh

Senior Product Manager (Asia):
Joyce Tan

Assistant Publishing Manager:
Pauline Lim

Production Executive:
Cindy Chai

Country Manager (China):
Caroline Ma

Account Manager (China):
Arthur Sun

Compositor:
Sok Ling Ong

For product information and technology assistance, contact us at
Cengage Learning Asia Customer Support, 65-6410-1200

For permission to use material from this text or product,
submit all requests online at **www.cengageasia.com/permissions**
Further permissions questions can be emailed to
asia.permissionrequest@cengage.com

ISBN-13: 978-981-4246-64-4
ISBN-10: 981-4246-64-6

Cengage Learning Asia Pte Ltd
5 Shenton Way
#01-01 UIC Building
Singapore 068808

Cengage Learning is a leading provider of customized learning solutions with office locations around the globe, including Andover, Melbourne, Mexico City, Stamford (CT), Toronto, Hong Kong, New Delhi, Seoul, Singapore and Tokyo. Locate your local office at **www.cengage.com/global**

Cengage Learning products are represented in Canada by Nelson Education, Ltd.

For product information, visit **www.cengageasia.com**

Photo credits:
Thinkstock, Getty Images

Printed in Singapore
1 2 3 4 5 15 14 13 12 11

Table of Contents

Listening

1. Listen to the audio recording and write the initials on the spaces provided.

(1) _____ā   _____ā

(2) _____á   _____á

(3) _____à   _____à

(4) _____è   _____è

(5) _____áo   _____áo

(6) _____òu   _____òu

(7) _____ài   _____ài

(8) _____ěn   _____ěn

(9) _____uā   _____uā

(10) _____én   _____én

(11) _____ā   _____iā

(12) _____ēn   _____īn

(13) _____í_____i   _____í_____i

(14) _____í___áng   _____í___áng

(15) _____ī___īn   _____ī___īn

(16) _____ù___ǒu   _____ù___ǒu

(17) _____ī_____ī   _____í_____ī

(18) _____ī___èi   _____ì___ei

(19) _____ī___ào   _____í___ào

(20) _____ào_____ǐ   _____āo_____i

(21) _____ī___ì   _____í_____ì

(22) ___ōng_____ī   ___ōng_____ī

2. Listen to the recording and write the finals with the tone marks in the spaces provided.

(1) b_____   b_____   (2) g_____   g_____

(3) h_____   h_____   (4) c_____   c_____

(5) b_____   b_____   (6) k_____   k_____

(7) n_____   n_____   (8) l_____   l_____

(9) h_____   h_____   (10) sh_____   sh_____

(11) k_____   k_____   (12) r_____   r_____

(13) d_____x_____   d_____x_____

(14) d_____r_____   d_____r_____

(15) g_____ch_____   g_____zh_____

(16) p_____z_____   p_____z_____

(17) r_____m_____   r_____m_____

(18) j_____h_____   j_____h_____

(19) ch_____t_____   ch_____t_____

(20) c_____y_____   c_____y_____

3. Listen to the recording and mark the tones.

(1) laoshı
(2) xıaozhang
(3) ayı
(4) pengyou
(5) xuesheng
(6) shushu
(7) tongxue
(8) zaoshang
(9) shangwu
(10) caochang
(11) jıaoshı
(12) jıntıan
(13) xıngqı
(14) dıanhua
(15) shubao

4. Listen to the recording and check the correct *pinyin* words.

(1) lǎobǎn ···◯   lóubǎn ···◯
(2) tūzi ···◯   tùzi ···◯
(3) chángcháng ···◯   Chángchéng ···◯
(4) Hànyǔ ···◯   Hányǔ ···◯
(5) míngtiān ···◯   měitiān ···◯
(6) lìshǐ ···◯   lìshí ···◯
(7) shuǐjiǎo ···◯   shuìjiào ···◯
(8) dàshī ···◯   dàshǐ ···◯

Read aloud the following *pinyin* words, paying attention to their tones. You may listen to the audio recording for reference.

1. The (first) tone followed by the first tone

fēijī	shūbāo	xīguā	xiāngjiāo
airplane	school bag	watermelon	banana

2. The (first) tone followed by the second tone

Zhōngguó	gōngrén	gōngyuán	kōngtiáo
China	worker	park	air-conditioner

3. The (first) tone followed by the third tone

gāngbǐ	qiānbǐ	shāngchǎng	jīnglǐ
pen	pencil	mall	manager

4. The (first) tone followed by the fourth tone

shūdiàn	jīdàn	shūcài	shūjià
bookstore	egg	vegetable	book shelf

5. The (first) tone followed by the neutral tone

zhuōzi	yīfu	chāzi	dāozi
table	clothes	fork	knife

6. The [second] tone followed by the first tone

máoyī	máojīn	yáshuā	yágāo
sweater	tower	toothbrush	toothpaste

7. The [second] tone followed by the second tone

yínháng	yóujú	shítáng	cháhú
bank	post office	cafeteria	teapot

8. The [second] tone followed by the third tone

niúnǎi	píngguǒ	cídiǎn	yóuyǒng
milk	apple	dictionary	swimming

9. The [second] tone followed by the fourth tone

máquè	pídài	cháyè	hóngsè
sparrow	leather belt	tea leaves	red color

10. The [second] tone followed by the neutral tone

júzi	chéngzi	pútao	sháozi
mandarin orange	orange	grapes	ladle

11. The (third) tone followed by the first tone

huǒchē	jǐngchē	xiǎomāo	shǔbiāo
train	police car	kitten	computer mouse

12. The (third) tone followed by the second tone

cǎoméi	wǎngqiú	huǒchái	xiǎohái
strawberry	tennis	matchstick	child

13. The (third) tone followed by the third tone

shuǐguǒ	xǐzǎo	xiǎogǒu	xǐliǎn
fruit	take a shower	puppy	wash face

14. The (third) tone followed by the fourth tone

lǎnduò	xiǎotù	pǎobù	xiězì
lazy	little rabbit	jog	write

15. The (third) tone followed by the neutral tone

běnzi	yǐzi	chǐzi	lǐzi
note book	chair	ruler	plum

16. The [fourth] tone followed by the first tone

qìchē	chènshān	dàyī	diàndēng
car	shirt	overcoat	light

17. The [fourth] tone followed by the second tone

dìtú	jiànpán	zàotái	fènghuáng
map	computer keyboard	stove	phoenix

18. The [fourth] tone followed by the third tone

diànnǎo	dìbǎn	xià yǔ	xià xuě
computer	floor	rain	snow

19. The [fourth] tone followed by the fourth tone

shuìjiào	diànshì	diànhuà	zhàoxiàng
sleep	television	telephone	take picture

20. The [fourth] tone followed by the neutral tone

kuàizi	kùzi	lìzi	shìzi
chopsticks	pants	chestnut	persimmon

21. The different tones for yi (一, one)

(1)	yī	shíyī	èrshíyī	sānshíyī
	sìshíyī	dì yī	dì shíyī	dì sānshíyī

(2)	yì zhāng	yì jīn	yì zhī	yì biān	yì bēi
	yì tái	yì zhí	yì hé	yì píng	yì tiáo
	yìqǐ	yìbǎ	yì běn	yì wǎn	yì diǎnr

(3)	yí cì	yí gè	yí jiàn	yí liàng	yígòng

22. The different tones for bu (不, no)

(1)	bù gāo	bù xīn	bù shuō	bù ān	bù tóng
	bù máng	bù xíng	bù lái	bù néng	bù chéng
	bù hǎo	bù mǎi	bù lěng	bù guǎn	bù gěi

(2)	bú qù	bú shì	bú gòu	bú huì	bú rè	bú zài

23. The suffix 儿

wánr	niǎor	huàr	zhèr	nàr
bīnggùnr	yíkuàir	xiǎomāor	xiǎoháir	
xiǎogǒur	yǔdiǎnr	xiǎoniǎor	miàntiáor	

Writing

1. Count the number of strokes in each character.

(1) 人 ____

(2) 口 ____

(3) 六 ____

(4) 女 ____

(5) 四 ____

(6) 五 ____

(7) 九 ____

(8) 你 ____

(9) 我 ____

(10) 他 ____

(11) 好 ____

(12) 是 ____

2. Identify the radical in each character and write it out.

(1) 他 ____

(2) 河 ____

(3) 课 ____

(4) 狗 ____

(5) 花 ____

(6) 家 ____

(7) 快 ____

(8) 打 ____

(9) 情 ____

(10) 你 ____

(11) 好 ____

(12) 这 ____

(13) 校 ____

(14) 吃 ____

(15) 跳 ____

Nice to meet you!

STEP 1 GREETING PEOPLE

Listening

1. Mike is greeting someone.
    QUESTION: Who is he greeting?
    Ⓐ His friend, David   Ⓑ His Chinese teacher, Miss Li   (   )

2. Mary is greeting someone. Listen and decide if she is greeting one person or many.
    Ⓐ One person   Ⓑ A group of people   (   )

3. Mr. Chen is greeting someone.
    QUESTION: Who is he greeting?
    Ⓐ A student in school   Ⓑ A class of students   (   )

4. Justin is back home. He greets two people as he comes in.
    QUESTION: Whom did he greet?
    Ⓐ His uncle and aunt   Ⓑ His father and mother   (   )

5. The teacher and students say something to each other.
    QUESTION: Are they going to start the class?
    Ⓐ Yes   Ⓑ No   (   )

Speaking

1. You meet the following people on the school grounds. How do you greet each of them?
    Ⓐ A history teacher, Mrs. Smith   Ⓑ A group of classmates   Ⓒ Your best friend

2. What would a child say to his/her parents before going to school?

3. How do you normally greet your teacher in class? What does your teacher say to you and your classmates?

4. Mike is being introduced to Uncle Wang. What would be the appropriate exchange between them?

9

1. Select the correct greetings that match the contexts depicted in the pictures.

Ⓐ "你好！"

Ⓑ "你们好！"

(   )

Ⓐ "你好！"

Ⓑ "再见！"

(   )

2. It is the first day of school. Class is just starting. Which of the following is the most appropriate exchange between the teacher and the students?

Ⓐ "你好！" "你好！"

Ⓑ "同学们好！" "老师好！"

Ⓒ "你们好！" "你好！"

Ⓓ "您好！" "再见！"

(   )

3. One of the following two greetings is to be placed on the badges for customer service officers. Which do you think is more appropriate?

Ⓐ 您好！

Ⓑ 再见！

(   )

Writing

1. Practice writing the following characters in the correct stroke order, then use them to form four greetings.

你 你 你 你 你 你 你

你

您 您 您 您 您 您 您 您 您 您 您

您

好 好 好 好 好 好

好

爸　爸爸爸爸爸爸爸爸

爸 | 爸 | 爸 | 爸 | | | | | |

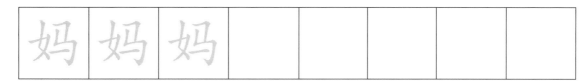

妈　妈妈妈妈妈妈

妈 | 妈 | 妈 | 妈 | | | | | |

Greeting 1: _____

Greeting 2: _____

Greeting 3: _____

Greeting 4: _____

2. Tom and Nina are joining a group of people to welcome a senior visitor at the airport. They need to make a greeting board. What should be on the board?

3. It is common to start with a word of greeting in an e-mail to friends. Help Xiaowei start his e-mail to two friends in China.

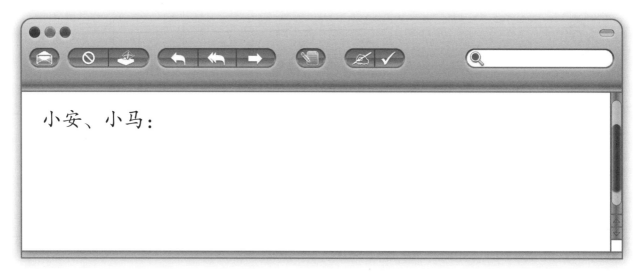

小安、小马：

4. Today is Tom's first day in school. The teacher has just introduced him to the class. Write what his classmates say and what he says in return.

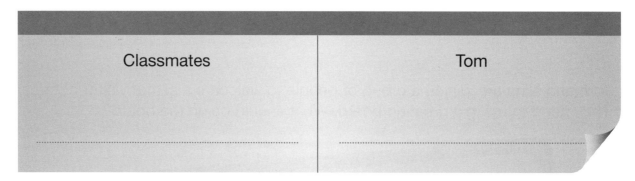

Classmates	Tom

1. A new student is introducing himself. Listen and tell who the person is.

    Ⓐ 马丁   Ⓑ 王小伟   Ⓒ 李芳芳   (   )

2. Mike is introducing you to a new friend. Listen and find out the person's name.

    Ⓐ 马丁   Ⓑ 王小伟   Ⓒ 李芳芳   (   )

3. There are some people talking in the room. Who are they?
    Select the correct answers.

    Ⓐ 王老师   Ⓑ 马丁   Ⓒ 小伟   Ⓓ 芳芳   (   )

Speaking

1. It is the first day of school. Everyone is to introduce himself/herself to the class.
    Introduce yourself to your class.

2. You are a team leader in a group of three with Mike and Lily. Introduce the three
    members of your group to the class.

Reading

1. Read the dialog and answer the questions.

    > A: 同学们好！我是李老师，他是张老师，她是王老师。
    > B: 老师们好！我是马丁。
    > C: 我是小伟。
    > D: 我是芳芳。

    QUESTIONS: 1) Who are the students? What are their names?

    _____

    2) How many teachers are there?

    _____

2. Mary found a name tag. Which of the following teachers does this tag belong to?

( )

3. Read the dialog on the picture below and label the rest of the people in the picture.

A: 我是Mark，他们是我同学。他是Jim，她是Lucy。
B: 她是谁？
A: 她是老师。

Mark

Writing

1. Practice writing the following characters in the correct stroke order.

我 我 我 我 我 我 我

我 | 我 | 我 | 我 | | | | |

他 他 他 他 他

他 | 他 | 他 | 他 | | | | |

她 她 她 她 她 她

她	她	她	她				

们 们 们 们 们

们	们	们	们				

是 是 是 是 是 是 是 是 是

是	是	是	是				

谁 谁 谁 谁 谁 谁 谁 谁 谁 谁

谁	谁	谁	谁				

2. Write the following words in Chinese.

   Ⓐ you (singular): _____   Ⓔ she: _____

   Ⓑ you (plural): _____   Ⓕ we: _____

   Ⓒ I: _____   Ⓖ they: _____

   Ⓓ he: _____

3. Your friend just came to the United States and wanted to know who the person on a dollar bill is. Answer the question in a full sentence. (The name of the person can be in English.)

他是谁? _____

STEP 3 ASKING HOW PEOPLE ARE

Listening

1. Listening rejoinder. Select the appropriate response to what you hear.

   Ⓐ 我不忙。　　Ⓑ 你好!　　Ⓒ 很好。谢谢! 　　　　　　　(　)

2. There are twins in your class. Listen and answer the question.

   QUESTION: Who is Ms. Zhang talking with?

   Ⓐ 小伟　　　　Ⓑ 小成 　　　　　　　　　　　　　　　(　)

3. School has been in session for a week. Ms. Zhang and Mark are talking to each other.

   QUESTION: 谁很忙?

   Ⓐ 张老师　　　Ⓑ Mark 　　　　　　　　　　　　　　(　)

Speaking

1. You met your former teacher. You haven't seen each other for a few months. You want to find out how he/she is doing now. What do you say?

2. Your dad just came home from work and looks tired. You want to show your concern. What should you say to him?

Reading

1. Read the text and select the correct response to the question.

   > 我很忙，很累。你好吗?

   Ⓐ 你好!　　　　Ⓑ 很好，谢谢!　　Ⓒ 再见。 　　　　　　　(　)

2. Choose the correct response from the box to the questions and statement below.
   1) 你是老师吗？　　（　　　）
   2) 你好吗？　　　　（　　　）
   3) 你累吗？　　　　（　　　）
   4) 你忙吗？　　（　　　）
   5) 再见！　　　（　　　）

   > **A** 再见！　　**B** 你好！　　**C** 还可以。谢谢！
   > **D** 不累。　　**E** 我不是。　　**F** 不忙。

Writing

1. Practice writing the following characters in the correct stroke order.

   吗 吗 吗 吗 吗 吗

吗	吗	吗	吗					

   很 很 很 很 很 很 很 很 很

很	很	很	很					

   好 好 好 好 好 好

好	好	好	好					

   忙 忙 忙 忙 忙 忙

忙	忙	忙	忙					

   不 不 不 不

不	不	不	不					

2. Practice writing the sentences below.

3. Two weeks have passed since school started. One of your classmates looks tired. Make a list of questions you want to ask him/her to show your concern.

_____

_____

_____

4. Your friend Xiaowei sent an e-mail to you. Read it and reply to his e-mail.

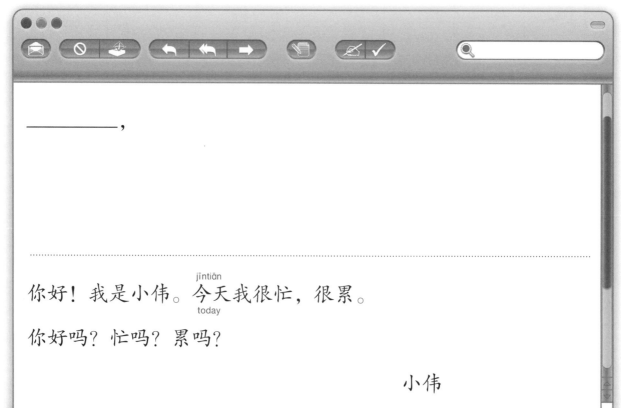

ASKING SOMEONE'S NAME

Listening

1. Listen to the introductions and match the names to the pictures.

2. Listening rejoinder. Select the most appropriate response to what you hear.
    1) Ⓐ 你好！　　Ⓑ 你好吗？　　Ⓒ 我很忙。　　Ⓓ 我叫李伟。（　　　）
    2) Ⓐ 他是小李。　Ⓑ 我不姓王。　Ⓒ 我姓李。　　Ⓓ 我叫小伟。（　　　）
    3) Ⓐ 他不是Mike。Ⓑ 我不忙。　　Ⓒ 他是小李。　Ⓓ 我叫李伟。（　　　）

3. Listen to the dialog and answer the questions.
    1) 老师姓什么？
       Ⓐ 王　　　　　　Ⓑ 张　　　　　　Ⓒ 李　　　　　　　　　　（　　　）

    2) 同学叫什么？
       Ⓐ 张小芳　　　　Ⓑ 李友　　　　　Ⓒ 王小芳　　　　　　　　（　　　）

Speaking

1. You are in a new class. How will you introduce your family name and given name?

2. You want to make new friends in your class. How do you ask for the names of other classmates?

1. The following is a dialog between two people. Read the four lines of dialog and number them in the correct order.

(　　　) 我姓张。

(　　　) 我是老师。你叫什么名字？

(　1　) 您好！您是老师吗？

(　　　) 我姓王，叫王小伟。老师，您贵姓？

2. Complete the following dialog by choosing the correct response for each blank.

1) A: 你好，小成！　　　　　2) A: 你好吗？
　 B: (　　　)　　　　　　　　　 B: (　　　)

3) A: 你忙吗？　　　　　　　4) A: 再见！
　 B: (　　　)　　　　　　　　　 B: (　　　)

5) A: 您贵姓？
　 B: (　　　)

❶很忙。　　❷很好。谢谢！
❸再见！　　❹我姓王。　　❺您好！

1. Practice writing the following characters in the correct stroke order.

叫 叫 叫 叫 叫

| 叫 | 叫 | 叫 | 叫 | | | | |

什 什 什 什

| 什 | 什 | 什 | 什 | | | | |

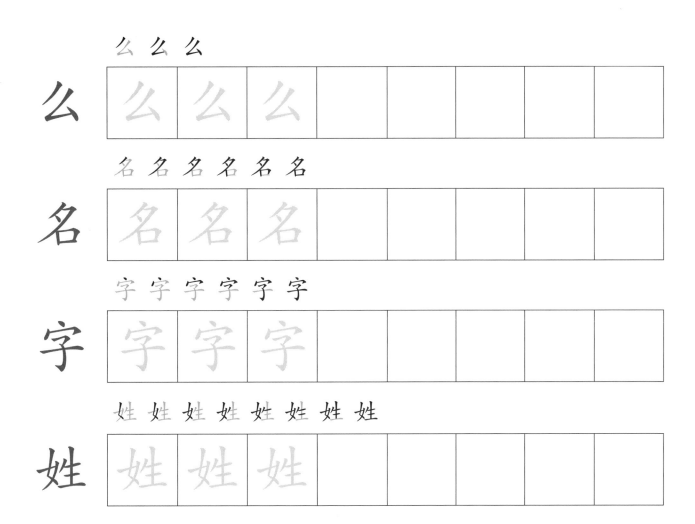

么　么　么

名　名　名　名　名　名

字　字　字　字　字　字

姓　姓　姓　姓　姓　姓　姓　姓

2. You are designing name tags for a party of new students. The words on the tag should greet people briefly, and introduce the person's full name.

3. Read the following e-mail from your pen pal in China and reply accordingly.

——————，

你好！
我姓王，叫王成。我很忙。你姓什么？你叫什么名字？
你好吗？

王成
2012-08-08

4. Your classmate is interviewing you with the questions below. Provide your answers based on a real life situation.

1) 你好吗？ _____

2) 你忙吗？ _____

3) 你叫小伟吗？ _____

4) 你姓什么？ _____

5) 你叫什么？ _____

Getting to know you

STEP 1 ABOUT ONE'S NATIONALITY

Listening

1. Two classmates, 丽丽 and 马丁, are talking about their nationalities. Listen and select the correct nationality for each of them.

   丽丽: (   )   马丁: (   )

   A 中国人   **B** 美国人   **C** 法国人   **D** 英国人

2. Mary is a new student. Her classmates are asking her questions about her nationality. Listen carefully and determine Mary's nationality.

   A 美国人   **B** 英国人   **C** 中国人   **D** 法国人   (   )

3. Two students are talking about their friend. Listen carefully and select the correct person they are talking about.

   A 王小成，美国人   **B** 王小伟，中国人
   C 王小伟，美国人   **D** 王小成，中国人   (   )

4. Listening rejoinder. What would be the most appropriate response to the question?

   A 我姓王。   **B** 我很忙。
   C 我也是北京人。   **D** 对，我也是美国人。   (   )

Speaking

1. Tell the following people's nationalities.

   A Harry Potter   **B** Mulan   **C** Superman   **D** Monkey King

2. You are at a party for new students. Introduce yourself including your name and nationality.

3. You are studying in a school in China and meet a Chinese student who speaks English with an American accent. You want to find out if she is also from the United States. What do you say to her?

1. You are helping to make name tags for new students. Read the students'
    information, then put each name onto the right tag below.

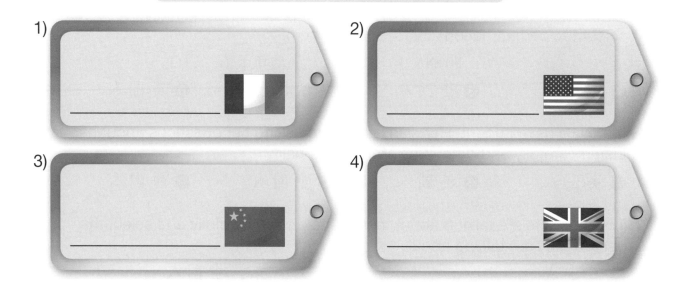

王小成是中国人。马丁是法国人。
芳芳是英国人。 小伟是美国人。

1)

2)

3)

4)

2. Some students are talking about their nationalities. Read the dialog and match
    the person to the correct nationality.

Lily：你好，Ben！
Ben：你好，Lily！你是美国人吗？
Lily：不是，我是中国人。芳芳也是中国人。我们都是中国人。
　　　你是美国人吗？
Ben：不是，我是英国人。Mary是美国人。

| Lily | 芳芳 | Mary | Ben |

| 美国人 | 英国人 | 中国人 |

3. Select the most appropriate answer to each of the questions below.

1) 你们好吗？ ( )
2) 你是哪国人？ ( )
3) 她是中国人吗？ ( )

Ⓐ 不，她是美国人。 Ⓑ 我们很好，谢谢！
Ⓒ 我是英国人。

Writing

1. Practice writing the following characters in the correct stroke order.

哪 哪 哪 哪 哪 哪 哪 哪 哪

哪　哪 哪 哪

国 国 国 国 国 国 国 国

国　国 国 国

人 人

人　人 人 人

美 美 美 美 美 美 美 美 美

美　美 美 美

中 中 中 中

中　中 中 中

对 对 对 对 对

对	对	对					

也 也 也

也	也	也					

都 都 都 都 都 都 都 都 都 都

都	都	都					

2. Write the nationality of each person below.

Ⓐ William Shakespeare _____

Ⓑ Martha Washington _____

Ⓒ Confucius _____

Ⓓ Napoleon Bonaparte _____

3. Fill in the blanks with the correct character(s).

> 是　都是　也是　哪国人　不是

1) Martin Luther King _____ 美国人，Isaac Newton _____ 美国人。

2) Jackie Chan _____ 中国人，Yao Ming _____ 中国人。

   他们 _____ 中国人。

3) Ⓐ 你是 _____? 　 Ⓑ 我是法国人。

4. One of the students plans to go to China. You are supposed to guess who the student is. You are allowed to ask yes-no questions about the person's family name, given name, nationality, etc. Write as many 吗 questions as possible.

5. Write an introduction of one of your classmates. Include his/her family name, given name and nationality.

STEP 2 ABOUT ONE'S HOMETOWN

Listening

1. Listening rejoinder. What would be the most appropriate response to the question?
   - Ⓐ 我是中国人。
   - Ⓑ 我叫马丁。
   - Ⓒ 我很好。
   - Ⓓ 我是北京人。

   (   )

2. Two classmates, 王伟 and 李芳, are talking about their hometowns. Listen and select the correct hometown each of them comes from.

   王伟：(   )   李芳：(   )
   - Ⓐ 北京
   - Ⓑ 上海
   - Ⓒ 西安
   - Ⓓ 香港

Speaking

1. You are helping to make students' profiles. Ask about their hometowns.

2. Imagine you are new to the class. Introduce yourself including your name, nationality and hometown.

Reading

1. Determine whether the statements are true (T) or false (F) based on the text below.

> 你们好！我姓王，叫小成。我是北京人。
> 他姓李，叫小伟，是上海人。她是王芳芳，
> 是西安人。

   1) 他们都是中国人。 (   )
   2) 他们都姓王。 (   )
   3) 小成是上海人。 (   )
   4) 芳芳是西安人。 (   )

2. Match the questions with the appropriate answers.

1) 你是哪国人？ •   • 不，我是上海人。

2) 她是哪里人？ •   • 他是北京人。

3) 你也是香港人吗？ •   • 我是美国人。

4) 他是哪里人？ •   • 她是西安人。

Writing

1. Practice writing the following characters in the correct stroke order.

里 里 里 里 里 里 里

里 | 里 | 里 | 里 | | | | |

北 北 北 北 北
京 京 京 京 京 京 京 京

北京 | 北京 | 北京 | | |

上 上 上
海 海 海 海 海 海 海 海 海 海

上海 | 上海 | 上海 | | |

2. Fill in the blanks with the appropriate words.

1) 你是_____? 我是香港人。

2) 你是上海人，他也是_____。

3) 我是北京人，你是西安人。我们_____中国人。

4) 我是香港人。你_____香港人吗？

STEP 3　ABOUT WHERE ONE LIVES

Listening

1. Listening rejoinder. What would be the most appropriate response to the question?

   Ⓐ 他是美国人。　　　　　Ⓑ 他家在中国。　　　　　(　　　)

2. Listening rejoinder. What would be the most appropriate response to the question?

   Ⓐ 我是中国人。　　　　　Ⓑ 我住上海东边。　　　　　(　　　)

3. Listen and answer the question.

   QUESTION: Mary 住哪儿?

   Ⓐ 东边　　　Ⓑ 南边　　　Ⓒ 西边　　　Ⓓ 北边　　　(　　　)

4. Listen to the locations of four cities in China, then determine their locations on the map by putting the correct number next to the name of each city.

   Ⓐ Shànghǎi (　　　)　　　　Ⓑ Xiānggǎng (　　　)

   Ⓒ Xī'ān　　(　　　)　　　　Ⓓ Běijīng　　(　　　)

5. A teacher is introducing four new students to the class. Listen carefully and match them with their countries.

中国	法国	美国	英国

马丁	丽丽	小伟	芳芳

6. A Chinese student is coming to visit your school in the United States. A host family is needed for him. Listen to the dialog between two classmates and see who lives nearby and can host the Chinese student.

   Who can help to host the visitor?

   Ⓐ Lily　　　　　　　Ⓑ 小芳　　　　　　　(　　　)

Speaking

1. Tell the names of at least four countries that you already know.

2. Students are talking about their homes. Tell where your home is and where you live now.

3. A new student joined your class today. Since you are trying to find a new carpool partner, ask him where he lives.

4. You are helping to collect data about students' homes. What question would you ask?

5. The teacher is asking where the students' homes are. Provide your answers based on the following picture.

   Example: 马丁家在哪儿？
   马丁家在东边。

Reading

1. Circle the direction characters that are found in each word.

   北京　东京　南京　西安　湖南　湖北　山东　山西

2. Your teacher is introducing three new students. Determine whether the four statements below are true (T) or false (F) based on the passage given.

   同学们好！这是马丁、芳芳、小伟。马丁是美国人，他家在美国。芳芳是中国人，她住北京南边。小伟是上海人，他家在上海。

   1) (　　　) 马丁、芳芳、小伟都是中国人。
   2) (　　　) 芳芳、小伟家在中国。
   3) (　　　) 马丁是英国人。

3. Read the seven lines of dialog between two students and number them in the correct order.

(　　) 不，我家在美国。

(　　) 我住这儿。你住哪儿？

(　　) 我家在香港。你家也在香港吗？

(1) 你好！

(　　) 你住哪儿？

(　　) 我也住这儿。你家在哪儿？

(　　) 你好！

4. Read the proverb below. Can you guess which English proverb has the same meaning?

东 南 西 北 ， 家 里 最 美 。
                          zuì
                    most nice

English proverb:_____

5. Match the questions with appropriate answers.

1) 你家在哪儿？ ●   ● 不，他是英国人。

2) 你住哪儿？ ●   ● 我家在中国。

3) 他也是美国人吗？ ●   ● 我是上海人。

4) 你是哪里人？ ●   ● 我住南边。

Writing

1. Practice writing the following characters in the correct stroke order.

家 家 家 家 家 家 家 家 家 家

家

在

在 在 在 在 在 在

在	在	在					

这

这 这 这 这 这 这 这

这	这	这					

那

那 那 那 那 那 那

那	那	那					

住

住 住 住 住 住 住 住

住	住	住					

东

东 东 东 东 东

东	东	东					

南

南 南 南 南 南 南 南 南 南

南	南	南					

西

西 西 西 西 西 西

西	西	西					

北 北 北 北 北

北

边 边 边 边 边

边

2. Write down the four directions on the map.

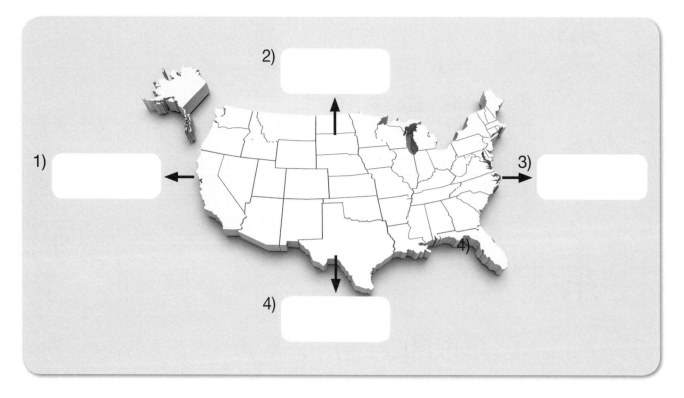

2)

1)

3)

4)

4)

3. 小伟 is close to you while 芳芳 is far from you. How will you describe their locations?

小伟在_____。

芳芳在_____。

4. Jenny is an international student from China. She promises to come to your birthday party. But since she can't drive, you decide to go and pick her up. Text her to find out where she lives.

5. Write a self-introduction and include as much information as possible.

6. You are helping your friend plan his trip to China. Write a sentence about each of the four major cities to describe its location.

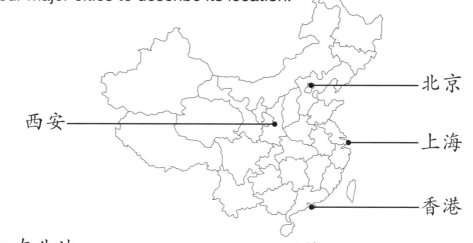

1) 北京 _在北边_____。   2) 上海 _____。

3) 香港_____。   4) 西安_____。

7. Two teachers (张芳芳, 马丁) and two students (小美, 小伟) live on campus during their summer program. Write a sentence about each person based on the picture.

   Example: 张芳芳老师是中国人。她住北边。

_____

_____

_____

What time is it?

STEP 1 COUNTING AND SAYING NUMBERS

Listening

1. Listen to a set of numbers. Cross out the number from the table when you hear it. In the remaining numbers, which has the greatest value.

_____

14	67	43
99	105	11
22	8	0

2. Your friend is telling you her telephone number. Write it in the boxes below.

3. You are going to hear nine numbers in three sets. Listen and write each set of three numbers. Then see if you can find the connection among them.

4. In the airport, the broadcast is telling which flights are delayed. Listen carefully and decide if Mary's flight (MU109) is among them.

Ⓐ Yes   Ⓑ No   ( )

Speaking

1. The assigned reading homework is p. 55, p. 56, p. 57 and p. 58. Tell your classmate who is absent today the page numbers for reading in Chinese.

2. Read aloud these two postal codes in China: 100080, 100875. Can you guess the city where these two places are located?

3. Look at the following calendar and tell the most likely dates Chinese couples might like for their wedding day.

February 2012 Calendar

Sunday	Monday	Tuesday	Wednesday	Thursday	Friday	Saturday
			1	2	3	4
5	6	7	8	9	10	11
12	13	14 Valentine's Day	15	16	17	18
19	20	21	22	23	24	25
26	27	28	29			

4. Read aloud the following tongue twister. How fast can you say it? Try reciting it a number of times to see how quickly you can say it.

123, 321, 1234567; 765, 567, 7654321

Reading

1. Convert these Chinese characters into Arabic numerals.

零 : _____   十六 : _____

三十五: _____   四十一 : _____

七十七: _____   一百零三: _____

2. Read the text below. Circle the characters that represent numbers and convert them into Arabic numerals. Do you know what this text is about?

> 一年有三百六十五天，十二个月。一个月有三十天或者三十一天，有时候有二十八天。一天有二十四小时，一小时有六十分钟，一分钟有六十秒。

_____

_____

3. Read the following message. How many numbers are there? Which school does the person attend?

> 我叫王一名，我住三零八号。
> hào
> number

_____

_____

4. The following set of numbers is in a logical pattern. Select the next number in the pattern.

> 一，三，五，七，九，_____

Ⓐ 七　　　　　　Ⓑ 十三　　　　　Ⓒ 十一　　　　　Ⓓ 四十四　　　(　)

1. Practice writing the following characters in the correct stroke order.

一

一

二 二

二

三 三 三

三

四 四 四 四 四

四

五 五 五 五

五

六 六 六 六

六

七 七

七

八

八 八

八 八 八

九

九 九

九 九 九

十

十 十

十 十 十

百

百 百 百 百 百 百

百 百 百

千

千 千 千

千 千 千

万

万 万 万

万 万 万

零

零 零 零 零 零 零 零 零 零 零 零 零 零

零 零 零

2. Write the following numbers in Chinese.

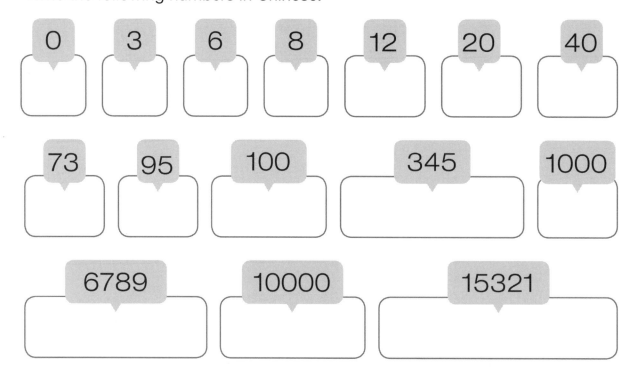

| 0 | 3 | 6 | 8 | 12 | 20 | 40 |

| 73 | 95 | 100 | 345 | 1000 |

| 6789 | 10000 | 15321 |

3. Write the answers in Chinese.

Ⓐ The number of letters in English: _____

Ⓑ The year the United States was founded: _____

Ⓒ The number you dial for emergency: _____

Ⓓ The total of your courses: _____

Ⓔ The number of your age: _____

Ⓕ The total of students in your class: _____

Ⓖ The total number of members in your family: _____

4. Make the biggest 5-digit number using numerals 1-5. Each number can only be used once. Then write it in Chinese.

DIFFERENT TYPES OF NUMBERS

Listening ✧

1. Listen to the rate between the U.S. dollar and the Chinese RMB. Fill in the blanks with the number you hear.

   Dollar ($): 美元 (měiyuán)　　RMB (¥): 人民币 (rénmínbì)　　$1 = ¥ (　　　　　　　)

2. Listen to the number pattern and select the next one in the pattern.

   Ⓐ 10　　　　　Ⓑ 11　　　　　Ⓒ 9　　　　　Ⓓ 8　　　　　(　　　)

3. Listen to the landmass ranking of the following countries. Number them in order of their ranking.

   (　　　) 美国　　(　　　) 法国　　(　　　) 中国　　(　　　) 英国

4. The teacher is announcing the result of a Chinese contest. Who is not among the first three winners?

   Ⓐ 小美　　　　Ⓑ 小英　　　　Ⓒ 小丽　　　　Ⓓ 小成　　　　(　　　)

Speaking ✧

1. Tell the ranking of the contestants in Chinese from the information given.

   | 1st: Lily | 2nd: Mary | 3rd: Lindsey |

2. Look at the tags and state the price from lowest to highest.

   $5.40　　　$2.70　　　$9.25　　　$2.85　　　$7.60

3. Students are giving donations to help children in Africa. The bank is helping to transfer the money. How much is the total sum of donation?

1. Below shows the population of each country. Rank the countries by their population.

| 1.3 billion | 61 million | 65 million | 310 million |

_____

_____

2. Beside are the temperature readings (in degree Celsius) of some classmates. Who is running a fever?

_____

Name	Temperature
David	三十七点一
John	三十八点六
Michelle	三十六点九
Joyce	三十七点四

Writing

1. Practice writing the following characters in the correct stroke order.

点 点 点 点 点 点 点 点 点

点

第 第 第 第 第 第 第 第 第 第 第

第

名 名 名 名 名 名

名

天 天 天 天

天

2. Four of you are dividing a pizza. How much does one get if you divide it equally?

Write it out in decimals first and then express it in Chinese. _____

3. The chart below shows the year and the average life expectancy in the United States. Read the numbers and fill in the blanks with the correct numbers <u>in Chinese</u>.

Year	Average life expectancy
1960	69.8
1970	70.8
1980	73.7
1990	75.2
2000	77
2005	77.7
2008	78.4

The longest age: _____ Year: _____

The shortest age: _____ Year: _____

The difference between the two: _____

4. Write five cities you want to visit. List them in order of preference using the pattern "第一是……". You may write the names of cities in English if you haven't learned their Chinese names.

_____

_____

_____

STEP 3 DIFFERENT SEGMENTS OF A DAY

Listening

1. Mary is talking about her preference for the time in the day. Number the following time segments in order of her preference.

   (   ) 上午   (   ) 中午   (   ) 下午   (   ) 晚上

2. Listen and select the time mentioned.
   - Ⓐ 今天下午
   - Ⓑ 明天上午
   - Ⓒ 今天上午
   - Ⓓ 明天下午   (   )

3. Listen to the short dialog.

   QUESTION: When will the person be in Beijing?
   - Ⓐ 今天
   - Ⓑ 昨天
   - Ⓒ 后天
   - Ⓓ 明天   (   )

4. Listen and answer the question in Chinese.

   QUESTION: When is Lily in China? _____ 。

Speaking

1. It's Saturday morning. Fangfang and her friends plan to play Frisbee over the weekend. Look at the weather forecast given and tell her when the best time would be for this outdoor sport.

今天 (Saturday)		明天 (Sunday)	
AM	PM	AM	PM
☀	🌧	🌧	☀

2. Mary's friends plan to visit her today (Friday) or tomorrow (Saturday). Check Mary's schedule and state when is not the good time to visit her.

今天 (Friday)		明天 (Saturday)	
上午	下午	上午	下午
having class	no class	no class	no class

3. The price of gas has undergone many changes in the past month. Write the highest and the lowest prices <u>in Chinese</u>, as well as the prices for yesterday and today (Feb 26th).

Highest: _____ Lowest: _____

昨天: _____ 今天: _____

Reading

1. Match the time with the segment of a day.

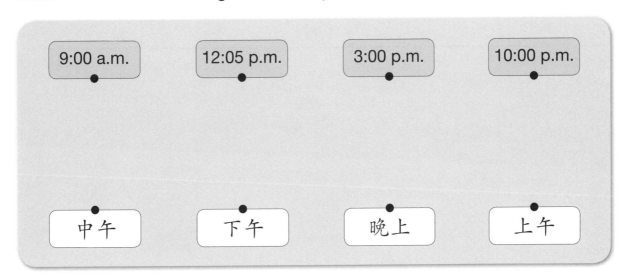

2. State the corresponding time segments for each pair of countries below.

   Ⓐ 美国：上午 ⟶ 中国：_____

   Ⓑ 英国：晚上 ⟶ 法国：_____

3. Xiaocheng's father is a stock market investor. Xiaocheng is reading an index report from the newspaper. What do you think Xiaocheng should tell his father about the market? It is getting better or worse?

   昨天上午：两千九百一十七点零八

   昨天下午：两千九百零六点三四

   今天上午：两千八百八十六点二二

   今天下午：两千八百零五点一七

   _____

   _____

4. Lily sent you a text message: 今天下午我在家。 If you want to visit her, when will you go to her home?

   _____

   _____

1. Practice writing the following characters in the correct stroke order.

下 下 下

下

早 早 早 早 早 早

早

午 午 午 午

午

晚 晚 晚 晚 晚 晚 晚 晚 晚 晚 晚

晚

昨 昨 昨 昨 昨 昨 昨 昨 昨

昨

今 今 今 今

今

明 明 明 明 明 明 明 明

明

2.   Write the time segments to which the following times belong.

   Ⓐ 9:00 AM _____

   Ⓑ 10:00 AM _____

   Ⓒ 12:00 PM _____

   Ⓓ 3:00 PM _____

   Ⓔ 10:00 PM _____

3 .   Study the timeline below and write the time words for each period.

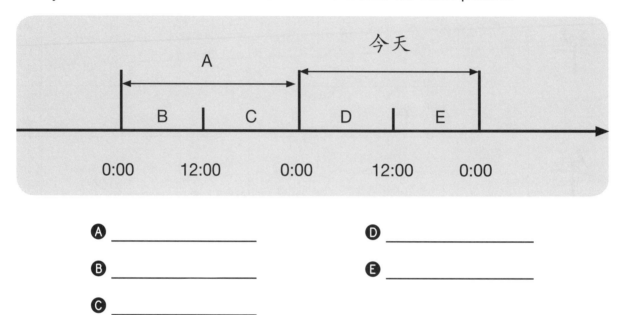

   Ⓐ _____   Ⓓ _____

   Ⓑ _____   Ⓔ _____

   Ⓒ _____

4.   Based on your real situation, write the time of day when the following activities take place.

   Have coffee: ....   Eat lunch: ....

   Watch TV: ....   Go to bed: ....

   Do homework: ....   Have classes: ....

   Play sports: ....   School ends: ....

STEP 4 ASKING AND TELLING TIME

Listening

1. A math teacher is saying a number. Listen carefully and write the numbers in Arabic numerals before writing them in Chinese.

   Arabic numerals: _____

   Chinese: _____

2. Listening rejoinder. Choose the statement that correctly answers the question.
   Ⓐ 我还可以。 Ⓑ 上午。 Ⓒ 我住这儿。 Ⓓ 现在十点十四分。 (   )

3. Mike is telling the time in his city. Listen and find out which is Mike's city.

   Ⓐ Paris (13: 57)

   Ⓑ London (12: 57)

   Ⓒ New York (07: 57)

   Ⓓ San Francisco (04: 57)   (   )

4. Lily is saying three important times in her daily life. Listen carefully and write the time in the following blanks. Then match the time with the activity she might do at these times of the day.

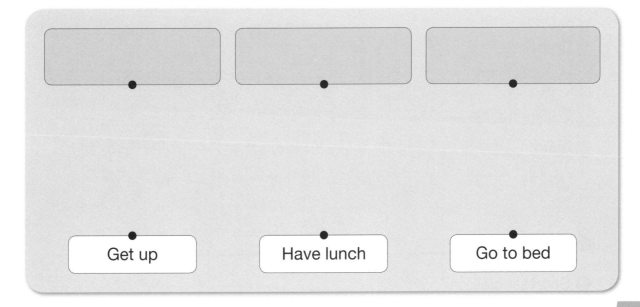

Get up   Have lunch   Go to bed

1. Answer the following question based on a real life situation.
   现在几点？

2. Your teacher is collecting car plate numbers for parking lot distribution. Tell your teacher the number on your parents' car plate. (If you can't remember it, make up one.)

3. What is your home phone number?

4. What is the postal zip code for your city?

Reading

1. The following are the beginning times of Anna's classes. Put the correct number into the blanks to show the order of her classes.

   第_____节：八点半
   <small>jié
period</small>

   第_____节：十一点半

   第_____节：九点二十五分

   第_____节：十点三刻

2. The following is a Chinese student's schedule. Which are his longest class and his shortest class?

Chinese	： 八点 — 八点三刻
English	： 八点五十五分 — 九点四十分
Whole school sports	： 九点五十分 — 十点二十五分
Math	： 十点二十五分 — 十一点二十五分
History	： 十点三十五分 — 十二点二十分

   Ⓐ Longest class: _____

   Ⓑ Shortest class: _____

3. Match the following columns.

1) 三百六十五 •   • The months in a year

2) 六十 •   • The hours in a day

3) 七 •   • The days in a year

4) 二十四 •   • The seconds in a minute

5) 十二 •   • The days in a week

4. Read the dialog and choose the correct answer to the questions.

A：你好！
B：我叫王小伟。你叫什么名字？
A：我叫张成。你是哪国人？
B：我是中国人。你是哪国人？
A：我也是中国人。现在几点？
B：差七分钟十二点。
A：谢谢！
B：不谢！再见！

1) 王小伟是哪国人？
Ⓐ 美国人   Ⓑ 英国人   Ⓒ 法国人   Ⓓ 中国人   (   )

2) 现在几点？
Ⓐ 12:00   Ⓑ 11:07   Ⓒ 12:07   Ⓓ 11:53   (   )

1. Practice writing the following characters in the correct stroke order.

现 现 现 现 现 现 现 现

现

几 几

几

分 分 分 分

分

秒 秒 秒 秒 秒 秒 秒 秒 秒

秒

刻 刻 刻 刻 刻 刻 刻 刻

刻

半 半 半 半 半

半

差 差 差 差 差 差 差 差

差

2. Write the following times in Chinese.

3. Write in Chinese the time for your daily schedule.

Daily Schedule

.... Get up

.... Breakfast

.... School starts

.... Lunch

.... School ends

.... Dinner

.... Go to bed

4. Lily is in Beijing airport to pick up her friend. She wants to know the time, but she doesn't have a watch. What would she say to the person with a watch? And if you were that person, how would you answer her? (Use the time of 4:57pm)

Lily:

You:

LESSON 4 What's today's date?

STEP 1 YEAR, MONTH, WEEK AND DAY

Listening

1. Listen and circle the date mentioned.
   - Ⓐ 2010年3月9日
   - Ⓑ 2011年9月20日
   - Ⓒ 2010年3月10日
   - Ⓓ 2011年9月30日   (   )

2. Listening rejoinder. Choose the correct response.
   - Ⓐ 今天星期六。
   - Ⓑ 今天九月十五号。
   - Ⓒ 今天九月。
   - Ⓓ 今天2011年。   (   )

3. Listening rejoinder. Choose the correct response.
   - Ⓐ 星期六
   - Ⓑ 星期四
   - Ⓒ 星期五
   - Ⓓ 星期一   (   )

4. Listening rejoinder. Choose the correct response.
   - Ⓐ 七月
   - Ⓑ 九月
   - Ⓒ 八月
   - Ⓓ 六月   (   )

Speaking

1. Answer the following question based on a real life situation.
   今天几号？星期几？

2. Imagine that the circled date is today. Tell today's date, tomorrow's date and yesterday's date.

October 2012						
SUN	MON	TUE	WED	THU	FRI	SAT
30	31					1
2	3	4	5	6	7	8
9	10	11	12	13	14	15
16	17	18	19	20	21	22
23	24	25	26	27	28	29

3. Grandma Li plans to visit the Northeastern United States. She doesn't like it too cold or too hot. In which months do you think she might want to go?

4. In which months do you go to school? In which months do you not go to school?

Reading

1. What is today's date and day based on the information below?

去年是二〇一〇年。昨天是星期一。明天是四月一日。

今天是_____年_____月_____日，

星期_____。

2. Read the sentence and fill in the blanks with the most appropriate answer.

丽丽星期一、星期二、星期三、星期四住在学校。
xuéxiào
school

她_____、 _____、_____住在家里。

3. Read the following calendar and fill in the blanks.

二〇一一年十月

星期日	星期一	星期二	星期三	星期四	星期五	星期六
						1 National Day, China
2	3	4	5	6	7	8
9	10	11	12	13	14	15
16	17	18	19	20	21	22
23	24	25	26	27	28	29
30	31					

1) 这个月是＿＿＿＿＿月。上个月是＿＿＿＿＿月。下个月是＿＿＿＿＿月。

2) 国庆节 (Guóqìng Jié, National Day) 是＿＿＿＿＿月＿＿＿＿＿号。

3) 十月二十六号是星期＿＿＿＿＿，二十九号是星期＿＿＿＿＿。

Writing

1. Practice writing the following characters in the correct stroke order.

年 年 年 年 年 年

年

前 前 前 前 前 前 前 前 前

前

去 去 去 去 去

去

后 后 后 后 后 后

后

月 月 月 月

月

号 号 号 号 号

号

号	号	号					

日 日 日 日

日

日	日	日					

2. Give the Chinese equivalents for the following time expressions.

1) the year before last: _____   9) this week: _____

2) last year: _____   10) last week: _____

3) this year: _____   11) next week: _____

4) next year: _____   12) the day before last: _____

5) the year after next: _____   13) yesterday: _____

6) this month: _____   14) today: _____

7) next month: _____   15) tomorrow: _____

8) last month: _____   16) the day after tomorrow: _____

3. Fill in the blanks in Chinese.

1) 今年是 2011 年。_____是 2012 年。_____是 2013 年。

_____是 2010年。_____是 2009年。

2) 这个月是十月。_____是九月。_____是十一月。

3) 今天是星期六。_____是星期五。_____是星期日。

_____是星期四。_____是星期一。

4. Refer to the calendar to answer the questions in full Chinese sentences.

NOVEMBER						
S	M	T	W	T	F	S
	1	2	3	4	5	6
7	8	9	10	11	12	13
14	15	16	17	18	19	20
21	22	23	24	25	26	27
28	29	30				

1) Which date is Thanksgiving?

_____

2) In which week does Thanksgiving fall, the 1st, 2nd, 3rd or 4th?

_____

STEP 2　COUNTING YEARS, MONTHS, WEEKS AND DAYS

Listening

1. Rita is planning to travel to Beijing. She is telling the dates on which she will be there. Listen and count how many days she plans to spend there.

   Ⓐ 七天　　　　Ⓑ 五天　　　　Ⓒ 八天　　　　Ⓓ 四天　　　　(　　)

2. David is telling the days in a week that he plays tennis. Listen and count how many days he plays tennis.

   Ⓐ 两天　　　　Ⓑ 四天　　　　Ⓒ 五天　　　　Ⓓ 三天　　　　(　　)

3. Anna is talking about today's date. Listen and choose the correct statement.

   Ⓐ 明天是12月1日。　　　　Ⓑ 明天是 2011 年1月1日。
   Ⓒ 昨天是 2009 年12月30日。　Ⓓ 昨天是12月31日。　　　　(　　)

4. Mike is studying in China. He is talking about his schedule. Listen and choose the correct statement.

   QUESTION: How many months will Mike stay in Beijing this year?

   Ⓐ 九个月　　　Ⓑ 十个月　　　Ⓒ 十一个月　　Ⓓ 三个月　　　(　　)

Speaking

1. Your Chinese friend wants to know about your school life. Give simple answers in Chinese based on a real life situation.

   1) How many days in a week do you go to school? How many days in a week do you not go to school?

2) How many months in a year do you go to school? How many months do you not go to school?

2. Provide some information about the American educational system to your Chinese friend. How many years does a student usually spend in elementary school, in secondary school, in high school, and in college in the United States?

3. Mark is a French student. Last year, he studied in the United States for the fall and winter terms. Then he went to study in China for the spring term and finally went back to France for the summer. How many months did he live in the United States, in China, and France? State your answer in Chinese.

Reading

1. Read the following passages and answer the questions by choosing the correct options.

    1)
    > 我家在中国。去年一月、二月、三月我在北京。十月、十一月、十二月在上海。四月、五月、六月、七月、八月、九月，我在美国。我在美国几个月？

    Ⓐ 四个月　　Ⓑ 三个月　　Ⓒ 六个月　　Ⓓ 十二个月　　　　( )

    2)
    > Lucy二〇一〇年、二〇一一年、二〇一二年、二〇一四年在英国。Lucy二〇一三年不在英国，她在法国。Lucy在英国几年？

    Ⓐ 四年　　　Ⓑ 三年　　　Ⓒ 七年　　　Ⓓ 六年　　　　　( )

2. Read Xiaocheng's schedule this year and answer the question in Chinese.

一月	二月	三月	四月	五月	六月
School	Home	School	School	School	School
七月	八月	九月	十月	十一月	十二月
Home	Home	School	School	School	School

QUESTION: How many months does Xiaocheng spend in school and at home this year?

ANSWER: _____

3. Determine whether the statements below are true (T) or false (F) based on the information provided below.

Name：王小成（中国北京人）

Experiences:
1995 —— 2001 北京 (elementary school)
2001 —— 2004 上海 (secondary school)
2004 —— 2007 西安 (high school)
2007 —— 2011 香港 (college)

1) 王小成是北京人。   (   )

2) 王小成在北京五年。   (   )

3) 王小成在上海三年。   (   )

4) 王小成在西安三年。   (   )

5) 王小成在香港四年。   (   )

Writing

1. Practice writing the following characters in the correct stroke order.

个　个　个

个

星　星　星　星　星　星　星　星　星
期　期　期　期　期　期　期　期　期　期　期　期

星期

2. Write the equivalent for each of the time periods below.

1) 一年　　　: _____ (months)

_____ (weeks)

_____ (days)

2) 一个星期: _____ (days)

3) 二月　　　: _____ (weeks)

4) 三月　　　: _____ (days)

3. Mark is an American college student. He plans to travel next summer. Here are his plans. Put the information into a narrative stating the time and place.

六月				七月		八月
Week 1 北京	Week 2 上海	Week 3 西安	Week 4 香港	Weeks 1 & 2 英国	Weeks 3 & 4 法国	美国

Example: 六月第一个星期，我在北京。

_____

_____

_____

STEP 3 AGE AND BIRTHDAY

Listening

1. You are in Beijing talking with a friend in New York. Listen and answer his question. *(Beijing is 12 hours ahead of New York.)*

   Ⓐ 九月二十八日；星期二；晚上九点十分
   Ⓑ 九月二十九日；星期三；早上九点十分
   Ⓒ 九月三十日；星期四；上午九点十分
   Ⓓ 九月二十八日；星期三；晚上九点十分   (   )

2. Listening rejoinder. Choose the correct response.

   Ⓐ 你好！   Ⓑ 我住在这儿。
   Ⓒ 明天星期四。   Ⓓ 祝你生日快乐！   (   )

3. Two friends are talking about their birthdays. Listen and answer the following questions.

   1) How old is Lily?

   _____

   2) Who is older, Xiaocheng or Lily?

   _____

3) What day is Xiaocheng's birthday this year?

_____

4. Your birthday is on November 19, the third Saturday of the month. You want to invite Uncle Jack to your party. Listen to Uncle Jack's message and see if he is able to come.

Ⓐ Yes　　　　　　　　　　　　　　Ⓑ No　　　　　　　　　(　　)

Speaking

1. This is part of the student list for your Chinese class. What questions do you need to ask to complete it?

Name	Age	Birthday
Mike	十五岁	?
Lily	?	十二月二十七日
Kathy	十七岁	?
王成	?	七月二十日

2. Tell your friend in Chinese today's date and the day of the week.

3. When is your birthday? What day is it this year? How old are you this year?

4. Introduce a family member including his or her age and birthday.

Reading

1. Here are your classmates' birthdays. Number them in order from young to old.
(　　　) Rick: 一九九六年十月一日
(　　　) Mary: 一九九七年一月七日
(　　　) Carl: 一九九六年五月二十一日
(　　　) Kate: 一九九七年九月十六日
(　　　) Mike: 一九九六年八月三日

2. Read the following dialog. Use the information in the dialog to note down Xiaocheng's and Lily's birthdays on the calendars.

Lily ：你好，我叫Lily，是美国人，你呢？

小成：你好！我叫小成，是中国人，我今年十六岁，你呢？

Lily ：我十五岁。我的生日是十月十七日，你的生日是几月几号？

小成：我的生日是三月三日。今年我的生日是三月的第一个星期六。你的生日是星期几？

Lily ：今年我的生日是十月的第三个星期二。

三月

星期日	星期一	星期二	星期三	星期四	星期五	星期六

十月

星期日	星期一	星期二	星期三	星期四	星期五	星期六

3. Read Mark's introduction of his family, circle everyone's birthday on the calendar and answer the following question. Who does Mark celebrate his birthday with?

Answer: _____

我叫马克，我是美国人，我十六岁。我的妈妈叫Kathy，她四十岁。我的爸爸的名字是Kevin，他四十二岁。我妈妈的生日是六月五日，爸爸的生日是六月三十日，我的生日也是六月三十日。

六月						
星期一	星期二	星期三	星期四	星期五	星期六	星期七
		1	2	3	4	5
6	7	8	9	10	11	12
13	14	15	16	17	18	19
20	21	22	23	24	25	26
27	28	29	30			

Writing

1. Practice writing the following characters in the correct stroke order.

岁 岁 岁 岁 岁 岁 岁

岁

多 多 多 多 多 多
大 大 大

多大

年 年 年 年 年 年
纪 纪 纪 纪 纪 纪

年纪 | 年纪 | 年纪 | | |

的 的 的 的 的 的 的 的

的 | 的 | 的 | 的 | | | | |

生 生 生 生 生
日 日 日 日

生日 | 生日 | 生日 | | |

呢 呢 呢 呢 呢 呢 呢 呢

呢 | 呢 | 呢 | 呢 | | | | |

祝 祝 祝 祝 祝 祝 祝 祝 祝

祝 | 祝 | 祝 | 祝 | | | | |

快 快 快 快 快 快 快
乐 乐 乐 乐 乐

快乐 | 快乐 | 快乐 | | |

节 节 节 节 节
日 日 日 日

节 日 | 节 日 | 节 日 | | |

2. Complete the last sentence with the correct information given in the first two sentences.

> 今天是二〇一一年十月二十六日，星期三。李叔叔这个星期天六十五岁。他的生日是_____年_____月_____日。

3. Fill in the blanks.

1) Lily 今年十五岁，_____十四岁，_____十六岁。

2) 今天是星期五，_____是星期四，_____是星期三，_____是星期六，_____是星期日。

3) 上个月是四月，这个月是_____，下个月是_____。

4) 明年是二〇一三年，今年是_____年，

4. Check the calendar and write down the dates of the following holidays this year in Chinese.

> 1) New Year's Day: _____
>
> 2) Independence Day: _____
>
> 3) Valentine's Day: _____
>
> 4) Halloween: _____
>
> 5) Thanksgiving: _____
>
> 6) Christmas: _____

5. This coming Saturday is Lily's birthday. Make her a birthday card in Chinese.

6. This coming Friday, May 6 is your friend Mary's 17th birthday. You are trying to order a birthday cake online for her birthday party of 20 people. Fill in the online order form in Chinese.

Online Cake Order

Name on the cake : _____

Age : _____   Birthday: _____

Wish : _____

_____

_____

Send

My family

STEP 1 ABOUT ONE'S FAMILY

Listening

1. Mary is introducing her family.
    QUESTION: Which of the following people is not mentioned?
    Ⓐ 父亲   Ⓑ 母亲   Ⓒ 哥哥   Ⓓ 妹妹   (   )

2. Listen to the question and choose the correct answer.
    Ⓐ 爷爷   Ⓑ 奶奶   Ⓒ 外公   Ⓓ 外婆   (   )

3. Mary and Mike are talking about a person.
    QUESTION: Who is that person?
    Ⓐ Mary 的哥哥   Ⓑ Mike 的哥哥   Ⓒ Mary 的姐姐   Ⓓ Mike 的姐姐   (   )

4. Mary and Marcy are twin sisters. They are introducing themselves to their new classmates.
    QUESTION: Do you know who the younger sister is?
    Ⓐ Mary   Ⓑ Marcy   (   )

Speaking

1. Your new classmate is showing you a photo of his four grandparents. How do you figure out who is who? What questions should you ask?

2. At a school community dinner for new students' families, your family is seated with Mary's family for the first time. Introduce your family members to them politely. (Based on a real life situation.)

3. In the first parents' conference, you are helping the teacher to arrange seating. You see Mike with a woman and a man. If you want to find out from Mike how these two persons are related to him, what question do you ask?

4. In a family get-together, you are going to meet your uncle and your aunt for the first time. How do you confirm with your father if the woman here is your aunt and the man over there is your uncle?

1. Read the introduction of Chris' family and fill in the family tree with the correct names.

> 这是 Chris，他哥哥是 Vincent。他爸爸是 Brad，妈妈是 Clair，姑姑是 Julie。他爷爷是 Bill，奶奶是 Rose。

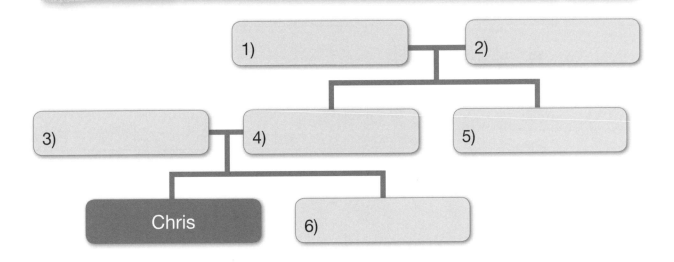

2. Determine whether the following statements are true (T) or false (F).
   1) 我爸爸的哥哥是我伯伯。　　（　　　）
   2) 我妈妈的母亲是我奶奶。　　（　　　）
   3) 我外公是我叔叔的父亲。　　（　　　）
   4) 我奶奶是我舅舅的母亲。　　（　　　）

3. There are five members in Xiaocheng's family: his parents, his younger sister and his grandpa. Read the following statements and fill in the blanks with correct choices.
   1) 她今年四十岁，她是老师。她很忙。她是谁？　　　　（　　　）
   2) 他今年六十七岁，他在家里，他不忙。他是谁？　　　（　　　）
   3) 她今年十三岁，她不忙。她是谁？　　　　　　　　　（　　　）
   4) 他今年十六岁，他很忙。他是谁？　　　　　　　　　（　　　）

   Ⓐ 爷爷　　Ⓑ 爸爸　　Ⓒ 妈妈　　Ⓓ 妹妹　　Ⓔ 小成

1. Practice writing the following characters in the correct stroke order.

父 父 父 父

父

母 母 母 母 母

母

亲 亲 亲 亲 亲 亲 亲 亲 亲

亲

哥 哥 哥 哥 哥 哥 哥 哥 哥 哥

哥

姐 姐 姐 姐 姐 姐 姐 姐

姐

弟 弟 弟 弟 弟 弟 弟

弟

妹 妹 妹 妹 妹 妹 妹 妹

妹

爷　爷 爷 爷 爷 爷 爷

爷 | 爷 | 爷 | 爷 | | | | |

奶 奶 奶 奶 奶

奶 | 奶 | 奶 | 奶 | | | | |

外 外 外 外 外

外 | 外 | 外 | 外 | | | | |

公 公 公 公

公 | 公 | 公 | 公 | | | | |

婆 婆 婆 婆 婆 婆 婆 婆 婆 婆 婆

婆 | 婆 | 婆 | 婆 | | | | |

伯 伯 伯 伯 伯 伯 伯

伯 | 伯 | 伯 | 伯 | | | | |

叔 叔 叔 叔 叔 叔 叔 叔

叔 | 叔 | 叔 | 叔 | | | | |

姑 姑 姑 姑 姑 姑 姑 姑

姑	姑	姑	姑				

舅 舅 舅 舅 舅 舅 舅 舅 舅 舅 舅 舅 舅

舅	舅	舅	舅				

2. Create your family tree with three generations: your grandparents, your parents and their siblings, you and your siblings. Write each person's name and how you are related to them.

3. Michelle shows Mike her family photo. Complete the following dialog between them.

Michelle : 这是我的家人。

Mike : _____?

Michell : 对。她是我妈妈。

Mike : 这是你妹妹吗?

Michelle : _____，这是我姐姐。

Mike : _____?

Michelle : 她十五岁。

Mike : 你几岁?

Michelle : _____。我们是双胞胎!
                               shuāngbāotāi   twins

NUMBER OF MEMBERS IN A FAMILY

Listening ⚡

1. Lucy is talking about her family. Listen and answer the question.
   QUESTION: How many people are there in Lucy's family?
   Ⓐ 三   Ⓑ 四   Ⓒ 五   Ⓓ 六   (   )

2. Listen to the dialog between Mary and Jack. Determine whether the statements below are true (T) or false (F).
   1) Mary 有弟弟。   (   )
   2) Jack 有哥哥。   (   )
   3) Mary 家有四口人。   (   )
   4) Jack 家有四口人。   (   )

3. Listening rejoinder. Choose the correct response to the question.
   Ⓐ 我弟弟   Ⓑ 我哥哥   Ⓒ 他   Ⓓ 我   (   )

4. Listen to Mary's introduction of her family and answer the question.
   QUESTION: Mary 家有几口人？
   Ⓐ 四   Ⓑ 五   Ⓒ 三   Ⓓ 六   (   )

Speaking ⚡

1. Introduce your family. State the number of members and include at least one sentence describing each person.

2. Look at Jenny's family. Describe her family.

Jenny

3. Your friend shows you a picture of him with his two sisters. Ask questions to confirm which of the two girls in the picture is his younger sister.

1. Read the text and answer the question.

> 我家有爸爸、妈妈、哥哥、姐姐、弟弟、妹妹和我。

我家有几口人?

Ⓐ 十口人　　Ⓑ 八口人　　Ⓒ 六口人　　Ⓓ 七口人　　(　　)

2. Read the paragraph and answer the questions.

> 芳芳是中国人。她家在中国北京。她家有五口人,她的父亲、母亲、弟弟、妹妹和她。他们住在北京东边。

1) In which city does Fangfang live?
   Ⓐ 北京　　Ⓑ 上海　　Ⓒ 香港　　Ⓓ 西安　　(　　)

2) How many people are there in Fangfang's family?
   Ⓐ 三　　Ⓑ 四　　Ⓒ 五　　Ⓓ 六　　(　　)

3. Read the two students' information and determine whether the statements below are true (T) or false (F).

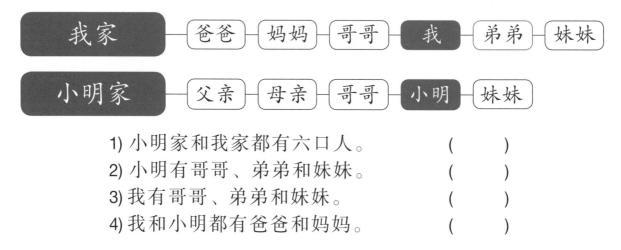

1) 小明家和我家都有六口人。　　(　　)
2) 小明有哥哥、弟弟和妹妹。　　(　　)
3) 我有哥哥、弟弟和妹妹。　　(　　)
4) 我和小明都有爸爸和妈妈。　　(　　)

1.　Practice writing the following characters in the correct stroke order.

有 有 有 有 有 有

有 | 有 | 有 | 有 | | | | |

口 口 口

口 | 口 | 口 | 口 | | | | |

和 和 和 和 和 和 和 和

和 | 和 | 和 | 和 | | | | |

2.　Below are two radicals. Write the characters you have learned that contain the radicals in them. Think about the connection between the radical and the meaning of the character.

亻: human

bó_____　nǐ_____　men_____　tā_____　zhù_____

口: mouth/measure word for people

hé_____　jiào_____　ma_____　nǎ_____　ne_____

3.　Write one sentence to introduce your family members using 有, 口 and 和.

4. Fill in the blanks.

我＿＿＿＿＿＿王，我＿＿＿＿＿＿王天明，我＿＿＿＿＿＿中国人。

我＿＿＿＿＿＿在北京。我家＿＿＿＿＿＿五口人，爷爷、奶奶、爸爸、

妈妈＿＿＿＿＿＿我。

5. Mary is having 小美 visit her home for the first time. They are talking about a picture on the wall. Complete the dialog.

Mary： 这是我的家人 (family members)。

小美： 你家有六口人吗？

Mary： ＿＿＿＿＿＿＿＿＿＿＿＿＿＿＿＿＿，他们是我爸爸、妈妈、姐姐、

哥哥、弟弟＿＿＿＿＿＿＿＿＿＿。

小美： ＿＿＿＿＿＿＿＿＿＿＿＿＿＿＿＿＿＿＿＿＿＿＿＿＿＿＿＿＿？

Mary： 不是，这是我弟弟。＿＿＿＿＿＿＿＿＿＿＿＿＿＿＿＿＿＿＿＿？

小美： 我家有三口人。

Mary： 你的爸爸、妈妈和你。

小美： ＿＿＿＿＿＿＿＿＿＿。我和爸爸、妈妈住在北京。

INTRODUCING ONE'S SIBLINGS

Listening ✨

1. Listening rejoinder. Choose the correct response.

   Ⓐ 这是我的哥哥。　　　Ⓑ 我的哥哥十六岁。

   Ⓒ 我家有四口人。　　　Ⓓ 我有两个哥哥。　　　（　　）

2. Listening rejoinder. Choose the correct response.

   Ⓐ 我妹妹有一个姐姐。　　Ⓑ 我没有妹妹。

   Ⓒ 我有一个姐姐。　　　Ⓓ 妹妹和我。　　　（　　）

3. Listen to the recording and answer the question.

   QUESTION: How many younger brothers does the person have?

   Ⓐ 一个　　　　　　　　Ⓑ 两个

   Ⓒ 三个　　　　　　　　Ⓓ 没有　　　　（　　）

4. Listen to the recording.

   QUESTION: Is the following statement true?

   我有一个哥哥，一个弟弟。（　　）

Speaking ✨

1. Below are Suzy's and Taylor's siblings. State the number of girls and boys in each picture, and then make a sentence for each using 有.

2. Study the information on Jerry's family and introduce his family members to your family using 口, 个 and 和.

爸爸	妈妈	哥哥	姐姐	妹妹
John	Lisa	两个 Jack 和 Jason	一个 Joan	一个 Julia

3. Introducing your siblings using 有 and 个.

Reading

1. Choose the correct answer for each question.

1) 爸爸的哥哥　　　　　(　　)　　　　6) 妈妈的哥哥和弟弟　(　　)

2) 爸爸的弟弟　　　　　(　　)　　　　7) 妈妈的姐姐和妹妹　(　　)

3) 爸爸的姐姐和妹妹　(　　)　　　　8) 妈妈的父亲　　　　(　　)

4) 爸爸的父亲　　　　　(　　)　　　　9) 妈妈的母亲　　　　(　　)

5) 爸爸的母亲　　　　　(　　)

Ⓐ 舅舅　Ⓑ 阿姨　Ⓒ 外公　Ⓓ 外婆　Ⓔ 爷爷
Ⓕ 奶奶　Ⓖ 伯伯　Ⓗ 叔叔　Ⓘ 姑姑

2. Jason 有三个姑姑，大姑四十九岁，二姑四十七岁，三姑四十二岁。他爸爸四十四岁。Jason 的爸爸有几个姐姐，几个妹妹？

Ⓐ 两个妹妹，一个姐姐。

Ⓑ 两个姐姐，两个妹妹。

Ⓒ 两个姐姐，一个妹妹。

Ⓓ 三个姐姐，没有妹妹。

(　　)

3. Your new friend in China sent you an e-mail to introduce herself and her family. Read the e-mail and determine whether the statements below are true (T) or false (F).

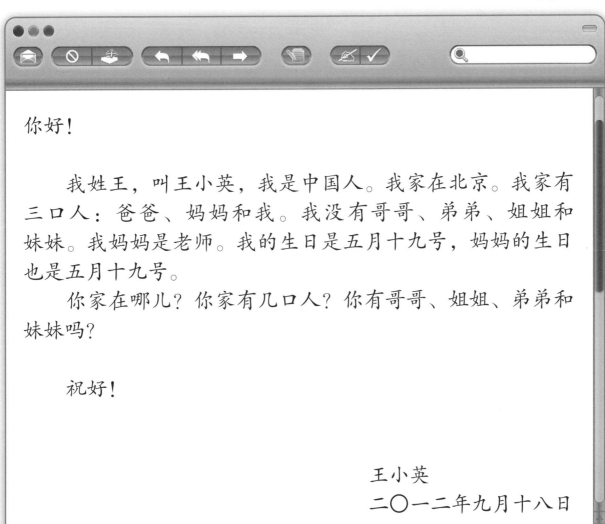

你好！

　　我姓王，叫王小英，我是中国人。我家在北京。我家有三口人：爸爸、妈妈和我。我没有哥哥、弟弟、姐姐和妹妹。我妈妈是老师。我的生日是五月十九号，妈妈的生日也是五月十九号。

　　你家在哪儿？你家有几口人？你有哥哥、姐姐、弟弟和妹妹吗？

　　祝好！

王小英
二〇一二年九月十八日

1) 小英有一个姐姐。　　　　　　　　　　（　　）
2) 小英没有哥哥，也没有弟弟。　　　　　（　　）
3) 小英家有三口人。　　　　　　　　　　（　　）
4) 小英的家在中国。　　　　　　　　　　（　　）
5) 小英的妈妈和小英的生日是同一天。（　　）

4. Your school is going to have a siblings' weekend. Read John's information card and find the picture that shows John with his siblings.

姓名	哥哥	姐姐	弟弟	妹妹
John	没有	没有	一个	一个

A

B

C

D

( )

Writing

1. Practice writing the following characters in the correct stroke order.

男 男 男 男 男 男 男

男 | 男 | 男 | 男 | | | |

女 女 女

女 | 女 | 女 | 女 | | | |

孩 孩 孩 孩 孩 孩 孩 孩 孩

孩

没 没 没 没 没 没 没

没

2. Complete the following sentences.

   Example: 芳芳的爸爸有一个妹妹和一个弟弟。芳芳有<u>一个姑姑</u>
   <u>和一个叔叔</u>。

   1) 我有两个叔叔。爸爸有 _____

   2) Lily有三个伯伯。Lily的爸爸有 _____

3. Answer the questions below about your family based on a real life situation.

   1) 你家有几口人？

   _____

   2) 你有姐姐和妹妹吗？

   _____

   3) 你有没有哥哥和弟弟？

   _____

4. Turn these statements into questions.

   1) 我家有四口人。 _____

   2) 她有三个姐姐。 _____

   3) 他是小伟的父亲。 _____

   4) 这是我爷爷。 _____

   5) 那是 Mary 的叔叔。 _____

5. Write an e-mail to your new friend 天明 with a short introduction of your siblings (make up one if you don't have one) and ask him about his families and siblings. Use 有, 没有, 有没有, 个, 口 and 和.

DESCRIBING PEOPLE

Listening ✦

1. Listen to the questions and choose the correct answers.

   1) (   )   2) (   )   3) (   )   4) (   )   5) (   )

   Ⓐ 爷爷   Ⓑ 叔叔   Ⓒ 外公   Ⓓ 奶奶   Ⓔ 舅舅

2. Vocabulary bingo. Listen to a series of words. Cross out the word from the table when you hear it. See if you have bingo.

弟弟	眉毛	耳朵	爷爷	父亲
胳膊	哥哥	腿	外公	伯伯
妈妈	脚	奶奶	手	肩膀
鼻子	妹妹	头发	Free space	肚子
叔叔	舅舅	阿姨	母亲	姑姑

3. Listen to Mike's introduction of his family. Determine whether the following statements are true (T) or false (F).

   1) Mike 有一个姐姐。   (   )
   2) Mike 家有两个女孩。   (   )
   3) Mike 没有哥哥。   (   )
   4) Mike 家里有三口人。   (   )
   5) Mike 的爸爸很高。   (   )

4. Listening rejoinder. Choose the correct response.

   1) Ⓐ 我家有四口人   Ⓑ 我爸爸四十五岁。

      Ⓒ 我有两个哥哥。   Ⓓ 我没有妹妹。   (   )

2) **Ⓐ** 我爸爸很高。　　　**Ⓑ** 我妈妈没有姐姐。

Ⓒ 他是我弟弟。　　　**Ⓓ** 这是我叔叔。　　　　　（　　）

1. Xiaomei is your Chinese neighbor. You plan to visit her home with your friend Xiaocheng. Here is a picture of her family. Make a brief introduction to Xiaocheng.

Xiaomei →

2. Kate is having a party at home. You see two young male family members in the room. What questions should you ask Kate to find out who the two men are?

3. Look at Fangfang's family tree. Describe it to your class.

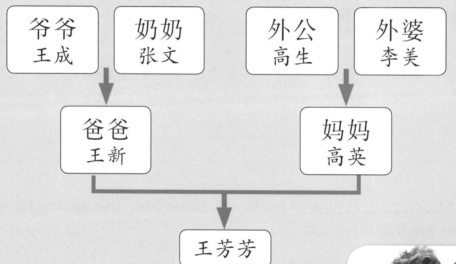

爷爷 王成　　奶奶 张文　　外公 高生　　外婆 李美

爸爸 王新　　妈妈 高英

王芳芳

4. Often a son looks like his father. Look at the picture and tell which of the son's facial features look like those of his father.

1. Draw lines to match the names with the body parts of the person.

眼睛 •

鼻子 •

胳膊 •

脚 •

• 头发

• 嘴

• 手

• 腿

2. Read the following introduction from a new friend, Mike, and choose the right picture for each person of Mike's family.

我家有四口人，爸爸、妈妈、姐姐和我。我爸爸四十二岁，他很高，也很胖。我妈妈四十岁，不胖不瘦。我姐姐十六岁，她很瘦。

A   B   C

D   E   F

1) 爸爸 (　　　)

2) 妈妈 (　　　)

3) 姐姐 (　　　)

87

3. Study Lily's family tree and answer the questions.

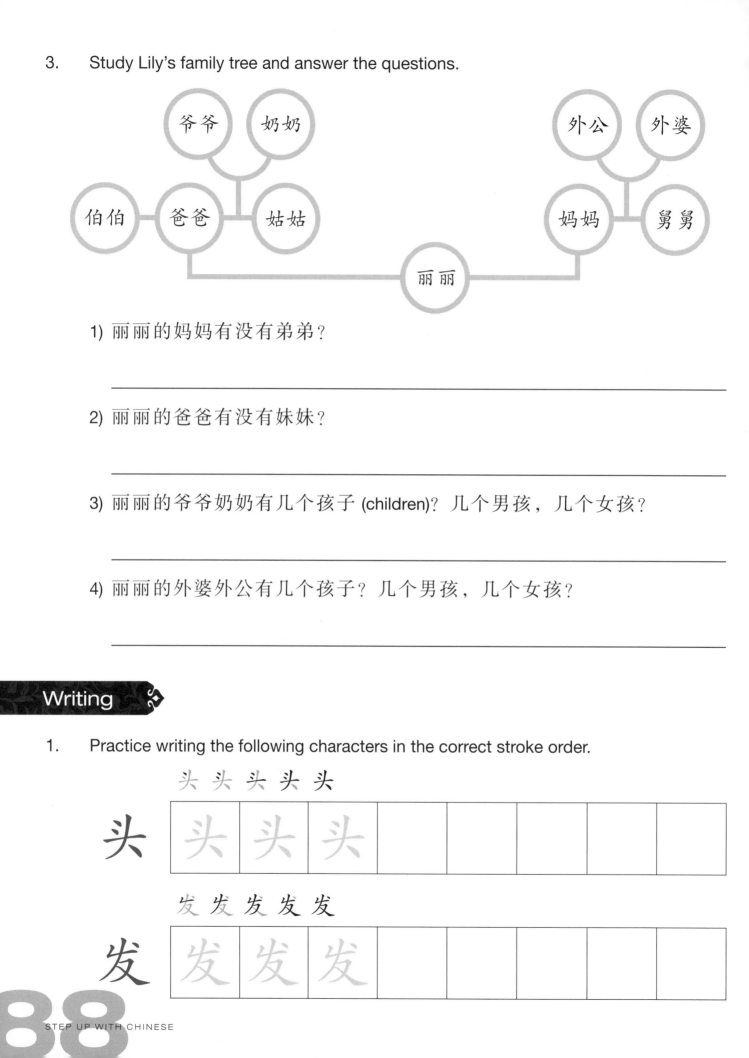

1) 丽丽的妈妈有没有弟弟？

_____

2) 丽丽的爸爸有没有妹妹？

_____

3) 丽丽的爷爷奶奶有几个孩子 (children)？几个男孩，几个女孩？

_____

4) 丽丽的外婆外公有几个孩子？几个男孩，几个女孩？

_____

Writing

1. Practice writing the following characters in the correct stroke order.

头 头 头 头 头

头

发 发 发 发 发

发

耳耳耳耳耳耳
朵朵朵朵朵朵

耳朵　耳朵　耳朵

子子子

鼻子　鼻子　鼻子

眼眼眼眼眼眼眼眼眼眼眼
睛睛睛睛睛睛睛睛睛睛睛睛

眼睛　眼睛　眼睛

嘴嘴嘴嘴嘴嘴嘴嘴嘴嘴嘴嘴嘴嘴嘴嘴
巴巴巴巴

嘴巴　嘴巴　嘴巴

手手手手

手　手　手　手

腿　腿　腿

脚 脚 脚 脚 脚 脚 脚 脚 脚 脚 脚

脚 | 脚 | 脚 | 脚 | | | | |

高 高 高 高 高 高 高 高 高 高

高 | 高 | 高 | 高 | | | | |

矮 矮 矮 矮 矮 矮 矮 矮 矮 矮 矮 矮 矮 矮

矮 | 矮 | 矮 | 矮 | | | | |

胖 胖 胖 胖 胖 胖 胖 胖 胖

胖 | 胖 | 胖 | 胖 | | | | |

瘦 瘦 瘦 瘦 瘦 瘦 瘦 瘦 瘦 瘦 瘦 瘦 瘦 瘦 瘦

瘦 | 瘦 | 瘦 | 瘦 | | | | |

2.   Each part of the body has its own function. Write the body part that corresponds to each of the following functions.

1) Walk: _____   4) Hear: _____

2) See: _____   5) Smell: _____

3) Talk: _____   6) Carry: _____

3. Write a short introduction of your family, including a brief description of each person's appearances.

_____

_____

_____

_____

Listening

1. Listening rejoinder. Choose the correct response.

   1) **Ⓐ** 我很好。   **Ⓑ** 再见!   **Ⓒ** 我是小伟。   (   )

   2) **Ⓐ** 他很忙。   **Ⓑ** 我不忙。   **Ⓒ** 我很好。   (   )

   3) **Ⓐ** 他很好。   **Ⓑ** 王老师好!   **Ⓒ** 他是我同学。   (   )

   4) **Ⓐ** 我姓张。   **Ⓑ** 李小成。   **Ⓒ** 还可以。   (   )

2. Listen to the descriptions and match them to the correct pictures.

1) _____   2) _____   3) _____   4) _____

3. Listen to the recordings and match them to the correct times.

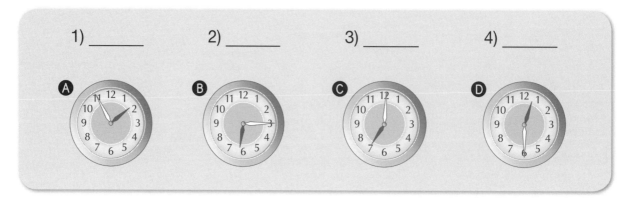

1) _____   2) _____   3) _____   4) _____

4. Listening rejoinder. Choose the correct response.

1) Ⓐ 西安人　　　Ⓑ 中国人　　　Ⓒ 上海人　　　　　　　(　)

2) Ⓐ 美国人　　　Ⓑ 香港人　　　Ⓒ 日本人　　　　　　　(　)

3) Ⓐ 对，我们都是美国人。　　　　　　　　　　　　(　)
　 Ⓑ 对，他也是中国人
　 Ⓒ 对，他是北京人。

5. Listen to the recording and mark out Mark's birthday on the calendar.

August						
Sun	Mon	Tue	Wed	Thu	Fri	Sat
			1	2	3	4
5	6	7	8	9	10	11
12	13	14	15	16	17	18
19	20	21	22	23	24	25
26	27	28	29	30	31	

6. Listen to the recording, find the word you hear, and write the corresponding number beside the word.

• 爷爷

妹妹 •　　　　　　　　　　　　　• 妈妈

• 　　　•
姐姐　　叔叔

• 　　　•　　　•　　　•
弟弟　　哥哥　　阿姨　　爸爸

Next, connect the points from 1 to 9 and then from 9 to 1. What do you get?

_____

7. Listen to the descriptions and match them to the correct pictures.

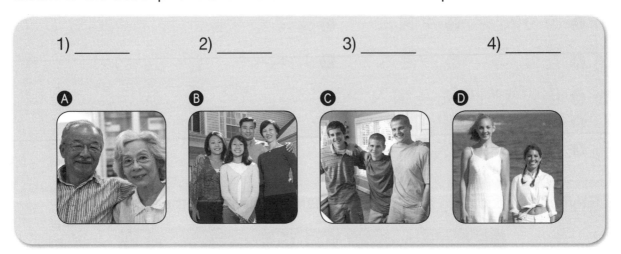

1) _____   2) _____   3) _____   4) _____

Ⓐ   Ⓑ   Ⓒ   Ⓓ

Speaking

1. Make a self-introduction following the example:

   你们好！我叫王小伟。我是美国人，我家在纽约。谢谢。再见。

2. Answer the questions about numbers in Chinese.
   1) How old are you?
   2) In which year were you born?
   3) What's your telephone number?
   4) What time did you get up today?
   5) What time does your first class begin?
   6) What time did you go to bed last night?
   7) How many months are there in one year?
   8) How many days are there in one year?
   9) How many hours are there in one day?
   10) What number should you call when you see a fire in China?
   11) What number should you call when someone needs an ambulance in China?
   12) How much is "π" when you calculate the circumference of a circle?
   13) How much RMB can be exchanged with one dollar?

3. **Game: Count without 7.** Count numbers in ascending order, one by one. The rule is to avoid saying the number 7 and any number associated with 7, such as 17, 27, 37, 47, and multiples of 7, such as 21, 28, 35, etc.

4. Answer the questions according to your personal life.
   1) 今天是星期几？明天呢？后天是几月几号？
   2) 你爸爸的生日是几月几号？星期几？
   3) 你妈妈的生日是几月几号？星期几？
   4) 你今年多大？
   5) 你的生日是几月几号？

5. Introduce your family members including their appearances.

Reading

1. Match the questions in column A to the correct answers in column B.

Column A	Column B
你好吗？ •	• 他很忙。
你妈妈累吗？ •	• 还可以。
你叫什么名字？ •	• 我姓张。
你爸爸忙吗？ •	• 她不累。
你姓什么？ •	• 我叫马克。
你爸爸是哪国人？ •	• 纽约。
你住哪儿？ •	• 他是美国人。
他也是美国人吗？ •	• 不是，他是法国人。

2. Read the following times and write the appropriate greetings for each of them.

   1) 七点 (am): _____   2) 三点 (pm): _____

   3) 十点半 (pm): _____   4) 十一点 (pm): _____

   5) 差一刻八点 (pm): _____

3. Steven went traveling with his mother over vacation. Here is a postcard written by him while they were traveling. Read it and answer the following questions in Chinese.

爸爸：

您好吗？忙不忙？

明天是新年，也是您的生日。我和妈妈祝您生日快乐、新年快乐！

我们在上海很好。我们下个星期二回家。再见！

Steven
2011年12月31日

1) To whom did Steven write this card?

_____

2) On which day did Steven write the postcard?

_____

3) What day is tomorrow?

_____

4) Where are they now?

_____

5) When will they come back home?

_____

4. Read the following sentences, and form questions for the answers given.

1) A: _____   B: 我有两个姐姐。

2) A: _____   B: 这是我妈妈。

3) A: _____   B: 我家有五口人。

4) A: _____   B: 她没有弟弟和妹妹。

5) A: _____   B: 是，他哥哥很高。

6) A: _____   B: 他是芳芳的叔叔。

7) A: _____   B: 对，那是我爸爸。

5. Read the short passage and answer the questions in Chinese.

> 我叫李明，今年十四岁。我家有五口人，爸爸、妈妈、弟弟、妹妹和我。
> 我爸爸今年四十岁，他很高、不胖。我妈妈三十九岁，她不高，很瘦。我弟弟和妹妹都很胖，他们今年四岁。

1) 李明多大了？

_____

2) 他家有几口人？有谁？

_____

3) 他爸爸高吗？

_____

4) 他妈妈胖吗？

_____

5) 他弟弟和妹妹瘦吗？

_____

1. Form phrases or sentences by matching the appropriate words with the one in the center. Write the sentences on the lines provided next page.

您　老师　很　姓　你　好　忙　再见　吗　同学们

_____

_____

_____

_____

2. Name two of your favorite celebrities and answer the following questions about them.

1) 他／她是哪国人？　　2) 他／她家在哪儿？

_____

_____

_____

_____

_____

3. The time in Beijing now is 10:15 a.m. Express in Chinese the corresponding time in other cities around the world.

1) 东京：_____　　2) 洛杉矶：_____
　Tokyo　　　　　　　　　　　　　Los Angeles

3) 伦敦：_____　　4) 新德里：_____
　London　　　　　　　　　　　　New Delhi

5) 上海：_____　　6) 悉尼　：_____
　　　　　　　　　　　　　　　　Sydney

4. Fill in the blanks with the appropriate words.

1) _____ 是 7 月 7 号。今天是 7 月 8 号。

2) 这个月是 9 月。_____ 是 10 月。

3) 今年是 2011 年。_____ 是 2010 年。_____ 是 2012 年。

4) 今天是你的生日，_____ 你生日 _____！

5) 你今年多大？我_____。

5. Complete the following sentences using 这, 那, 是, 在 and 有.

1) _____ 是我爸爸，_____ 是我哥哥。

2) 我没_____ 哥哥，我_____ 弟弟。

3) 我_____ 一个哥哥和一个姐姐。

4) 她_____ 我姐姐，她_____ 我妈妈。

5) 叔叔_____ 一个男孩，一个女孩。

6) 这_____ 我家人，我们家_____ 两个孩子。

6. Read the following words or phrases and rearrange them to form sentences.

1) 名字　爸爸　什么　你　叫

   _____

2) 十点　现在　一刻　差

   _____

3) 祝　快乐　生日　你

   _____

4) 很　爸爸　矮　弟弟　高　很

   _____

My family pet

STEP 1 TYPES OF ANIMALS

Listening

1. Listening rejoinder. Choose the correct response.

   Ⓐ 我没有狗。   Ⓑ 我有猫，还有鱼。

   Ⓒ 这是猴子。   Ⓓ 马很高。   (   )

2. The zookeeper is talking about the animals in the zoo. Listen and find out what they do not have now.

   Ⓐ 狮子   Ⓑ 老虎   Ⓒ 大熊猫   Ⓓ 猴子   (   )

3. You are going to hear a description of an animal. Choose the one that fits the description.

   Ⓐ 鸡   Ⓑ 鸟   Ⓒ 蛇   Ⓓ 羊   (   )

4. The Jade Emperor is announcing the final results of the animals' race for zodiac calendar placement. Listen and number the correct order for the twelve animals.

   牛 (   )   兔 (   )   猪 (   )   羊 (   )

   鸡 (   )   蛇 (   )   马 (   )   虎 (   )

   lóng
   龙 (   )   shǔ
   鼠 (   )   猴 (   )   狗 (   )
   dragon   rat

Speaking

1. Your younger sister wants to buy a pet. Tell her the animals in the pet store (there are dogs, cats, fish, birds and rabbits). Start with 这里有…

2. You are visiting a zoo and want to ask a friend to join you. Tell him or her as many animals as possible that are in the zoo. Use 有…还有….

3. You are in a zoo and see an animal in an enclosure. What question should you ask the zookeeper to find out what this animal is?

4. You are visiting a friend who has many pets. You want to know what pets he has to make sure you won't have an allergy attack. What questions should you ask?

1. Circle the animals that are commonly kept as pets.

老虎	猫	狮子	猴子	兔子
鱼	牛	猪	羊	马
鸡	狗	蛇	鸟	

2. The Chinese zodiac consists of twelve animals which follow a fixed sequence. Each year the Chinese calendar is represented by one of these twelve animals, according to the sequence. Study the sequence below and answer the questions.

鼠（shǔ／mouse），牛，虎，兔，龙，蛇（lóng／dragon），马，羊，猴，鸡，狗，猪。

QUESTIONS: 2010年是虎年，2009年是什么年？ ＿＿＿＿＿＿＿＿＿＿＿＿

2011年是什么年？ ＿＿＿＿＿＿＿＿＿＿＿＿

3. Read the text and answer the question.

这个动物不高也不大，有很大的耳朵。 这是什么动物？

Ⓐ 猫　　　　Ⓑ 虎　　　　Ⓒ 马　　　　Ⓓ 兔子　　　　（　　）

4. Read the paragraph below. Determine whether the following statements are true (T) or false (F).

Mike 家有很多宠物，有猫、狗、鱼、鸟、兔子，还有马。Mike 的猫很大很胖，叫 Mimi，今年三岁。Mimi 的生日是十月十二日。明天是 Mimi 的生日。

1) Mike家有很多动物。（　　） 2) Mimi很胖。（　　）

3) Mike的猫三岁。（　　） 4) 今天是十月十一日。（　　）

1. Practice writing the following characters in the correct stroke order.

狗 狗 狗 狗 狗 狗 狗 狗

狗

| 狗 | 狗 | 狗 | | | | | |

猫 猫 猫 猫 猫 猫 猫 猫 猫 猫 猫

猫

| 猫 | 猫 | 猫 | | | | | |

鱼 鱼 鱼 鱼 鱼 鱼 鱼 鱼

鱼

| 鱼 | 鱼 | 鱼 | | | | | |

鸡 鸡 鸡 鸡 鸡 鸡 鸡

鸡

| 鸡 | 鸡 | 鸡 | | | | | |

猪 猪 猪 猪 猪 猪 猪 猪 猪 猪 猪

猪

| 猪 | 猪 | 猪 | | | | | |

鸟 鸟 鸟 鸟 鸟

鸟

| 鸟 | 鸟 | 鸟 | | | | | |

羊 羊 羊 羊 羊 羊 羊

羊

| 羊 | 羊 | 羊 | | | | | |

牛 牛 牛 牛

牛 | 牛 | 牛 | 牛 | | | | |

马 马 马

马 | 马 | 马 | 马 | | | | |

兔 兔 兔 兔 兔 兔 兔 兔

兔 | 兔 | 兔 | 兔 | | | | |

蛇 蛇 蛇 蛇 蛇 蛇 蛇 蛇 蛇 蛇 蛇

蛇 | 蛇 | 蛇 | 蛇 | | | | |

虎 虎 虎 虎 虎 虎 虎 虎

虎 | 虎 | 虎 | 虎 | | | | |

猴 猴 猴 猴 猴 猴 猴 猴 猴 猴 猴 猴

猴 | 猴 | 猴 | 猴 | | | | |

还 还 还 还 还 还 还

还 | 还 | 还 | 还 | | | | |

2. List at least eight farm animals.

_____

_____

_____

3. List the Chinese zodiac animals in the correct order. Follow the example.

第一个，鼠。 _____

_____

_____

4. Mary visits a pet store and is having a talk with the shop assistant. Complete the dialog.

Mary　　　：你好！

Assistant：你好！

Mary　　　：这里的宠物很多，它们都很好看！
　　　　　　　　　　　　　　　　　　　　kàn
　　　　　　　　　　　　　　　　　nice looking

Assistant：谢谢！_____?

Mary　　　：我没有宠物。_____?

Assistant：这是南美的鸟。

Mary　　　：_____?

Assistant：对，那是狗。那是中国的小狗。

Mary　　　：_____?

Assistant：有，我们有英国猫和中东猫。

Mary　　　：很好！谢谢你！再见！

Assistant：再见！

EXPRESSING LIKES AND DISLIKES

Listening 🎧

1. Listening rejoinder. Choose the correct response.

    Ⓐ 小鸟是宠物。　　　Ⓑ 我没有鸟。

    Ⓒ 我很喜欢小鸟。　　Ⓓ 我不喜欢小猫。　　　　　（　　）

2. Listening rejoinder. Choose the correct response.

    Ⓐ 这是狗。　　　　　Ⓑ 那是猫。

    Ⓒ 我最喜欢狗。　　　Ⓓ 我没有蛇。　　　　　（　　）

3. Listen to a description of Jerry. Determine whether the following statements are true (T) or false (F).

    1) Jerry has birds and fish.　　　（　　）
    2) Jerry likes Harry the cat most.　（　　）
    3) Harry likes the rabbit most.　　（　　）
    4) Harry dislikes the cat most.　　（　　）

4. Lily's birthday is coming. Her father is planning to get her a pet as a present. Listen to the dialog and help Lily's father decide what to buy for her.

    Ⓐ cat　　　Ⓑ bird　　　Ⓒ rabbit　　　Ⓓ dog　　　（　　）

Speaking 🎤

1. A new zoo is going to be set up. The zoo management is seeking public feedback on what animals to have. Tell them the animals you would like them to consider.

2. You are doing research of your classmates' pets. You need to collect information on what pet(s) they have and what animal they like the most. What are the two questions you need to ask?

3. Look at the picture. What animal is this? Does your family have one? Do you like this animal?

4. Talk about your pet, i.e. what it is, its name, birthday, etc. If you don't have one, talk about whether you like animals and your favorite animal. Or, you can make up an imaginary pet.

Reading

1. Read the dialog. Determine whether the following statements are true (T) or false (F).

A: 这是什么动物？
B: 这是我的狗。
A: 你的狗很大！
B: 它七岁，是英国狗。你喜欢狗吗？
A: 我喜欢狗，也喜欢猫。我最喜欢兔子！
B: 我不喜欢猫，也不喜欢兔子。

1) A 不喜欢狗。(　　　)
2) B 没有狗。　(　　　)
3) A 最喜欢猫。(　　　)
4) B 不喜欢兔子和猫。　(　　　)

2. Choose the correct answers to the questions.

小丽喜欢很多动物。老虎、狮子、熊猫、猴子，还有蛇，她都喜欢。

小丽喜欢的动物里，

1) 什么动物是中国的？　　　(　　　)　　Ⓐ 熊猫　　Ⓑ 老虎
2) 什么动物没有手，也没有脚？(　　　)　　Ⓒ 狮子　　Ⓓ 蛇

她家有很多宠物，有狗、兔子、猫、鸟和鱼。

她家的宠物里，

3) 什么动物没有手，也没有脚？(　　　)　　Ⓐ 狗　　Ⓑ 兔子　Ⓒ 猫
　　　　　　　　　　　　　　　　　　　　　Ⓓ 鸟　　Ⓔ 鱼

3. Read the text. In the table, draw three happy faces for "like most" and three unhappy faces for "dislike most."

> 动物园有很多动物。男孩们最喜欢狮子、老虎和猴子。女孩们最喜欢熊猫和小鸟。他们都不喜欢蛇。

	狮子	熊猫	老虎	小鸟	猴子	蛇
男孩						
女孩						
☺ like most　　☹ dislike most						

4. Read the text and match the items in the middle with the two on each side.

> 北京人喜欢动物，他们最喜欢鸟和鱼，他们最不喜欢猫。美国人也喜欢动物，他们最喜欢狗，最不喜欢蛇。

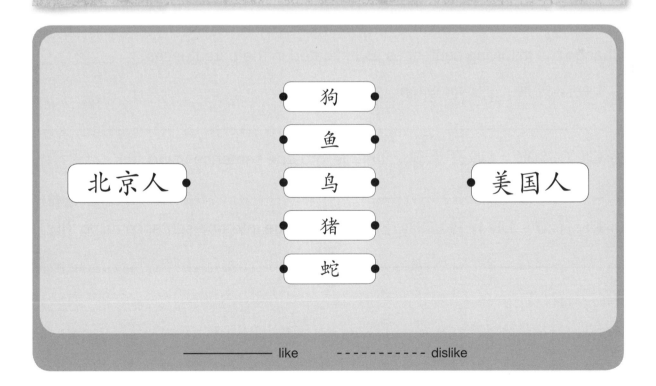

―――――― like　---------- dislike

1.   Practice writing the following characters in the correct stroke order.

喜欢

宠物

最 最 最 最 最 最 最 最 最 最 最

最

2.   Change the following sentences as indicated in the parentheses.

1) Lily喜欢狗。(吗 question)

_____

2) Lily喜欢狗。Lily喜欢猫。(merge into one sentence using 也)

_____

3) Lily有狗。Lily有鸟。Lily还有鱼。(merge into one sentence using 和)

_____

3. Mike wants to get to know his new friend, Jacky. He writes an e-mail to find out Jacky's attitude toward pets, animals and zoos. Help him make at least three questions with 喜欢不喜欢.

4. The table below shows Xiaowei's family's preference for pets. Write a summary using (最) 喜欢 and (最) 不喜欢.

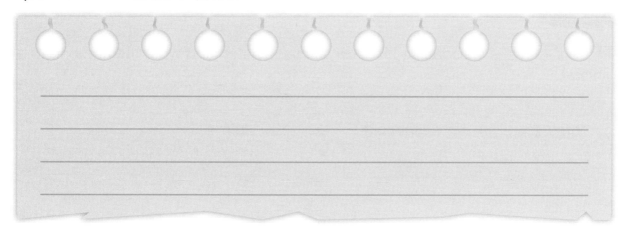

家人	狗	猫	鱼	鸟
爸爸	♥♥	♥		
妈妈	♥♥♥		♥♥♥	♥
小伟	♥♥♥	♥		♥♥♥

Listening

1. Mr. McDonald is introducing his farm animals. Listen and write the number for each animal.

   horse (   )   sheep (   )   cow (   )

   cat (   )   dog (   )   Fish (   )

2. Listening rejoinder. Choose the correct response.

   Ⓐ 我喜欢熊猫。

   Ⓑ 这是一只熊猫。

   Ⓒ 我不喜欢熊猫。

   Ⓓ 有，动物园有很多只熊猫。 (   )

3. Listen and determine whether the following statements are true (T) or false (F).

   1) Jack不喜欢动物。 (   )

   2) Jack有十只狗。 (   )

   3) Jack最喜欢狗。 (   )

   4) Jack的狗是中国狗。 (   )

4. Ben is taking his first tour of a zoo. He is asking questions about the animals. Listen and mark a "✔" for the animals he knows and a "✘" for those he doesn't know.

   猴子 (   )   老虎 (   )   狮子 (   )   熊猫 (   )

Speaking

1. The pictures on the right show the animals Uncle Wang has. Say what animals he has and how many using appropriate measure words.

2. State what pets you have and how many. Express it in one sentence based on your personal life. (If you do not have a pet, make up one.)

3. Mary is very afraid of dogs and snakes. She's visiting Jane's home. What question should she ask?

4. Read aloud this tongue twister and see how fast you can recite it.

一匹马，两头牛，三条小鱼水里游；四只虎，
_{shuǐ}
water

五只猴，六头小猪乐悠悠。
_{yōu}
leisurely

Reading

1. Read the sentence and draw a picture to illustrate it.

Mike 喜欢宠物，他家有两条大鱼，两条小鱼，还有三只小鸟和一只猫。

2. Match the measure words to the appropriate animals.

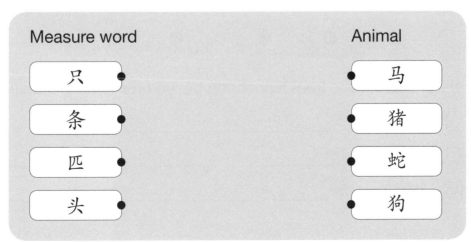

Measure word
只
条
匹
头

Animal
马
猪
蛇
狗

3. Two students and a teacher are talking about a new animal in the zoo. Read the ten lines of dialog and put them in the correct order by numbering them from 1 to 10.

(   ) Mike，你好！

(   ) 不是。

(   ) 那是一只熊猫。

(   ) 也不是。

(   ) Tom，那是什么动物？

(   ) 我不知道 (not sure)，那是一只猫吗？

(1   ) 你好，Tom!

(   ) 那是一只熊吗？

(   ) 老师，那是什么动物？

(   ) 谢谢！

4. Read the following paragraph and choose the right answers to the questions.

我叫小成，我很喜欢小动物。我家里有很多宠物。我弟弟有三只猫，我有两只狗，我妹妹还有八条鱼。我最喜欢的动物是熊猫，我不喜欢蛇。你喜欢什么动物？你不喜欢什么动物？你有什么宠物？

QUESTIONS:
1) What pets does Xiaocheng's brother have?   (   )
2) What pets does Xiaocheng's sister have?   (   )
3) What is Xiaocheng's favorite animal?   (   )
4) What animal does Xiaocheng like the least?   (   )

Ⓐ 狗   Ⓑ 猫   Ⓒ 熊猫   Ⓓ 蛇   Ⓔ 鱼

Next, answer the questions from Xiaocheng based on a real life situation:

5) 你喜欢什么动物？ _____

6) 你不喜欢什么动物？ _____

7) 你有什么宠物？ _____

1. Practice writing the following characters in the correct stroke order.

只 只 只 只 只 只

只 | 只 | 只 | 只 | | | | |

条 条 条 条 条 条 条

条 | 条 | 条 | 条 | | | | |

头 头 头 头 头 头

头 | 头 | 头 | 头 | | | | |

匹 匹 匹 匹 匹

匹 | 匹 | 匹 | 匹 | | | | |

2. Write the correct measure word for each animal.

猫 (　　) 　　牛 (　　) 　　鱼 (　　)

狗 (　　) 　　猴子 (　　) 　　兔子 (　　)

蛇 (　　) 　　猪 (　　) 　　老虎 (　　)

马 (　　) 　　狮子 (　　) 　　羊 (　　)

3. You are doing a pet survey among your classmates. The aim is to find out how many of your classmates have a pet, and how many of them have dog(s) as pet. Make up two questions you need to ask to complete the form. Use 有没有.

QUESTION 1: _____

QUESTION 2: _____

4. Write an e-mail to your Chinese pen pal introducing your pet(s) and how many you have. If you don't have one, talk about your favorite animal. Next, ask if he/she has pet(s), guess what pet(s) he/she has and ask about his/her favorite animals. (Write at least 10 sentences, using 有没有, 最喜欢, and proper measure words.)

Listening ✦

1. Listen and choose the correct answer to the question.
   QUESTION: What pet does the person have?

   Ⓐ dog   **Ⓑ** pig   **Ⓒ** cat   **Ⓓ** bird   (   )

2. Listen to the action word and choose the right animal or pet.

   Ⓐ fish   **Ⓑ** horse   **Ⓒ** bird   **Ⓓ** rabbit   (   )

3. Listen and choose the correct answer on how the animal moves.

   Ⓐ fly   **Ⓑ** crawl   **Ⓒ** run   **Ⓓ** swim   (   )

4. Listen and answer the question with "yes" or "no."
   QUESTION: Does the child like crawling? _____ .

Speaking ✦

1. State how these animals move.
   Sample: 老虎跑。

   狗   鸟   蛇   鱼   兔子

2. Talk about your preference for these movements: running, jumping, swimming and crawling.
   Use 最喜欢, 最不喜欢, and 也.

3. Talk about your favorite animal and how it moves.

1. Match the following verbs with the correct pictures.

 飞   跑   爬   游   跳

2. 鸡飞狗跳，人跑马叫。 What kind of scene does this idiom describe?

    A quiet   **B** happy   **C** noisy   **D** serious   (   )

3. Read the sentence and draw a picture of it.

    天上有两只鸟在飞，一只大鸟，一只小鸟。
    sky

1. Practice writing the following characters in the correct stroke order.

2. Correct the mistakes in the paragraph.

动物园有很多动物。老虎在飞，小鸟在爬，蛇在跳，鱼在跑。我喜欢动物园里的动物。

_____

_____

_____

3. Complete the following sentences using appropriate verbs.

小鸟_____。 马_____。

兔子_____。 鱼_____。

蛇 _____。

4. Fill in the blanks with 和, 也 or 还.

1) 我有一只猫_____一只狗。

2) 芳芳有三条鱼_____一匹马。

3) 小明家的小狗喜欢跑，_____喜欢跳。

4) 动物园有狮子、老虎、蛇、猴子，_____有很多鸟。

STEP 1 DESCRIBING ONE'S SCHOOL

Listening

1. A senior student is introducing the school to a new student. Listen to the conversation and identify the facilities on the school map by marking them with the corresponding letters.

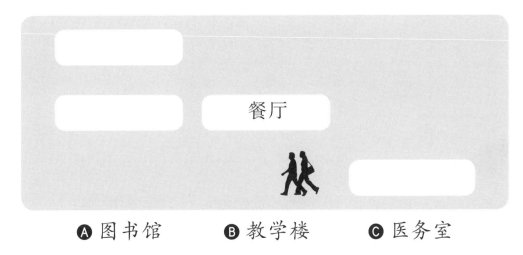

Ⓐ 图书馆   Ⓑ 教学楼   Ⓒ 医务室

2. Mark is talking about his family picture. Listen to what he says and choose the right picture.

( )

3. Mike wants to know about his new school, so he is asking his teacher a question. Listen and choose the correct responses.

Ⓐ Mike 你好！体育馆离餐厅不远。

Ⓑ Mike 你好！我们学校有一个体育馆和两个医务室。

Ⓒ Mike 你好！我们学校的餐厅不大，学校里还有一个图书馆。

Ⓓ Mike 你好！我们学校的体育馆在教学楼的旁边。

( )

4. A teacher is introducing the location of students' homes. Circle the mistake in this map.

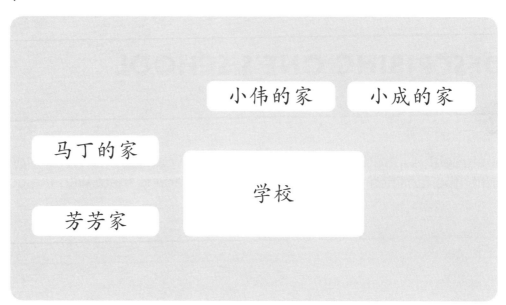

Speaking

1. Below is Kathy's schedule. Use this information to state the places where Kathy goes for the activities. Follow the example.

Example: 早上八点，Kathy在教室。

	Kathy's schedule				
TIME	8:00 a.m.	12:00 p.m.	1:00 p.m.	3:00 p.m.	4:00 p.m.
ACTIVITY	Attending classes	Lunch	Basketball	Reading	Online research

2. You are a new student and you are lost on campus. On your right is a sports field and on your left is a cafeteria. The library is in front of you. Imagine that you are calling your friend on your cell phone for help. Describe your location to her so that she can help you get home.

1. Match the characters, *pinyin*, and English.

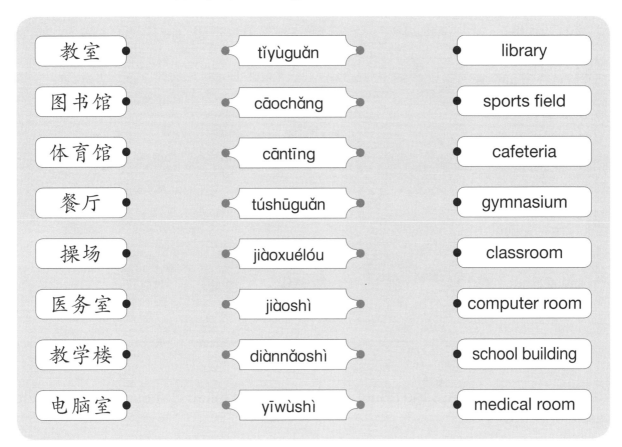

教室	tǐyùguǎn	library
图书馆	cāochǎng	sports field
体育馆	cāntīng	cafeteria
餐厅	túshūguǎn	gymnasium
操场	jiàoxuélóu	classroom
医务室	jiàoshì	computer room
教学楼	diànnǎoshì	school building
电脑室	yīwùshì	medical room

2. Read the following riddles and try to guess what characters they are.

1) 门的左边是一个人。

_____

2) 心的上边有个你。

_____

3) 日的右边有个月。

_____

4) 可的上边还是可。

_____

3. Read the following text and assign seats by writing the names in the blanks.

明天我们和爷爷、奶奶、叔叔、阿姨，还有叔叔阿姨的
孩子小伟一起看电影。爷爷奶奶坐在前边。小伟在叔叔和
阿姨中间。爸爸在叔叔的旁边，我在爸爸和妈妈的中间。

| Row 20 | | | | No.19 | No.20 | |

_____ _____

| Row 21 | No.17 | No.18 | No.19 | No.20 | No.21 | No.22 |

_____ _____ _____ _____ _____ _____

4. Read the following passage about a school in the United States and answer the questions in Chinese.

我在友好中学上学。我们学校在北京的东边，学校里有
八百多个学生，一百多位老师。学校里有五个教学楼，一个
体育馆，一个医务室，一个餐厅，一个电脑室，还有一个图
书馆。餐厅在电脑室的右边，在医务室的旁边。体育馆的前
边是图书馆。体育馆离餐厅很远，离医务室也很远。

QUESTIONS:

1) 友好中学在哪儿？ _____

2) 餐厅在哪儿？ _____

3) 体育馆的前边是什么？ _____

4) 餐厅离体育馆远不远？ _____

5) 医务室离电脑室远吗？ _____

1. Practice writing the following characters in the correct stroke order.

教 教 教 教 教 教 教 教 教 教 教

教 | 教 | 教 | 教 | | | | |

室 室 室 室 室 室 室 室 室

室 | 室 | 室 | 室 | | | | |

馆 馆 馆 馆 馆 馆 馆 馆 馆 馆 馆

馆 | 馆 | 馆 | 馆 | | | | |

场 场 场 场 场 场

场 | 场 | 场 | 场 | | | | |

里 里 里 里 里 里 里

里 | 里 | 里 | 里 | | | | |

外 外 外 外 外

外 | 外 | 外 | 外 | | | | |

2. Describe the facilities in your school using 里 and 外.

_____

_____

_____

3. Lily is planning a weekend trip with her dad. They live in China. They have only two days and cannot go too far. Complete the dialog.

丽丽：爸爸，我们去美国，好吗？
qù
go

爸爸：不好，1) _____ 。

丽丽：我们去加拿大，好吗？

爸爸：也不好，2) _____ 。

丽丽：那我们去日本，好吗？

爸爸：好，3) _____ 。

丽丽：4) _____ ？

爸爸：日本在中国的东边。

4. Jack is in front of two buildings. He is not sure if the building on his left is the school gymnasium or not. He texts his friend to confirm. What text should he write?

To:

New Message   Cancel

Send

DESCRIBING ONE'S CLASSROOM

Listening ✦

1. Lily is talking about her classroom. Listen to what she says and determine whether the following statements are true (T) or false (F).

    1) 教室右边的墙上有一块黑板。 （　　）
    2) 学生桌椅前边的墙上有一个钟。 （　　）
    3) 门旁边有一张地图。 （　　）

2. Listen to the classroom setup and mark the objects on the picture with the corresponding letters.

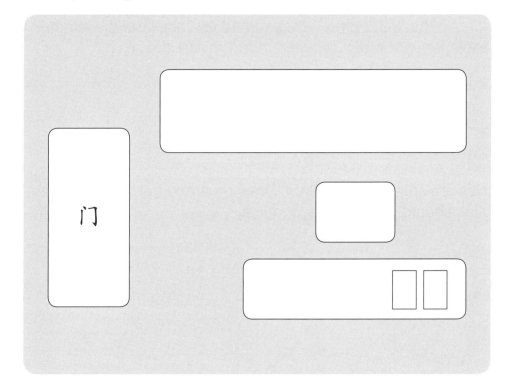

Ⓐ 老师的桌子
Ⓑ 老师的椅子
Ⓒ 两本书
Ⓓ 黑板

3. Mike, Lily and John's items are mixed together. Listen to what each of them is saying about their items and write their names under the correct picture of the item.

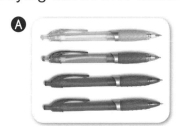　　　　

_____　　_____　　_____

4. Lily is going to her art class, but her pencil case is missing. Listen and choose the best response to the question.

Ⓐ 我没有尺子。　　Ⓑ 行，给你。　Ⓒ 不行，我只有一张纸。　（　　　）

Speaking

1. You found a backpack in the school cafeteria. It contains two red books and a blue pencil case with three pens, a pencil and a green ruler in it. Make a phone call to the Lost and Found desk and report what is in the bag.

2. Make a poster of your favorite classroom, using the new words given. Present it to your class using 有 and the appropriate measure words.
   (窗户, 门, 墙, 桌子, 椅子, 黑板, 钟, 地图, 书)

3. You left your school backpack at home. What should you ask your classmates to borrow the basic tools for your math, drawing, and English classes?

Reading

1. Lily's school supplies are spread on the floor. Draw an arrow from the supplies to where the supplies should go in the second line.

2. Read the following introduction of Annie's classroom. Correct the mistakes based on the picture below.

　　教室的墙上有一块黑板。黑板前边有九张桌子。桌子上有很多书。窗户在桌子旁边的墙上。

_____

_____

_____

3. Read the two columns below and match them correctly.

1) 我没有铅笔。　　　　　　　　是一个黑色的钟。

2) 椅子上有什么？　　　　　　　我有。给你。

3) 你有橡皮吗？　　　　　　　　不近，很远。

4) 借我一把尺子，行吗？　　　　在我的书包里。

5) 文具袋里有什么？　　　　　　有一个绿色的书包。

6) 书在哪儿？　　　　　　　　　有三只红色的铅笔。

7) 椅子离黑板近吗？　　　　　　我没有。

8) 地图的旁边是什么？　　　　　行，给你。

1. Practice writing the following characters in the correct stroke order.

窗 窗 窗 窗 窗 窗 窗 窗 窗 窗 窗 窗

窗 | 窗 | 窗 | | | | |

桌 桌 桌 桌 桌 桌 桌 桌 桌 桌 桌

桌 | 桌 | 桌 | | | | |

椅 椅 椅 椅 椅 椅 椅 椅 椅 椅 椅

椅 | 椅 | 椅 | | | | |

墙 墙 墙 墙 墙 墙 墙 墙 墙 墙 墙 墙

墙 | 墙 | 墙 | | | | |

钟 钟 钟 钟 钟 钟 钟 钟 钟

钟 | 钟 | 钟 | | | | |

支 支 支 支

支 | 支 | 支 | | | | |

张 张 张 张 张 张 张

张 | 张 | 张 | | | | |

把

把把把把把把把
把	把	把					

本

本本本本本
本	本	本					

块

块块块块块块块
块	块	块					

包

包包包包包
包	包	包					

笔

笔笔笔笔笔笔笔笔笔笔
笔	笔	笔					

尺

尺尺尺尺
尺	尺	尺					

书

书书书书
书	书	书					

借

借借借借借借借借借
借	借	借					

行 行 行 行 行 行 行

行 | 行 | 行 | 行 | | | | | |

给 给 给 给 给 给 给 给 给

给 | 给 | 给 | 给 | | | | | |

2. School is about to start. Here are the items that you need for the new term. Write your preferred color for each of the items.

书包 ➔ 蓝色的书包_____

铅笔 ➔ _____

文具袋 ➔ _____

尺子 ➔ _____

圆珠笔 ➔ _____

橡皮 ➔ _____

3. Write a letter to your Chinese friend describing your classroom and ask what his/her classroom looks like. (100 characters)

Listening

1. Mike is talking about his courses this year. Check it against Mary's courses below and see how many courses they both have. Choose the correct number of courses that they have in common.

Mary's courses 2012				
英语	数学	历史	物理	音乐

Ⓐ 3   Ⓑ 2   Ⓒ 4   Ⓓ 1   (   )

2. Jacky wants to have some guidance on how to learn physics and chemistry from Tom. Listen and see which subject Jacky should approach Tom for.

Ⓐ Chemistry   Ⓑ Physics   (   )

3. Xiaowei and Mark are talking about last year's courses. Listen and write the courses they took below each of their names.

小伟		Mike
_____	英文 化学 美术	_____
_____	体育 音乐 生物	_____
_____	物理 历史 中文	_____
_____	电脑 地理	_____

4. It's the first day of school. Mark and Xiaowei are talking about their schedules. Listen to the dialog and identify which schedule is Mark's and which is Xiaowei's.

Schedule 1		星期一	星期二	星期三	星期四	星期五
上午		数学	英语	数学	英语	历史
		电脑	数学	英语	电脑	数学
		地理	地理	电脑	历史	英语
下午		英语	历史		地理	电脑
			电脑		数学	

Schedule 2		星期一	星期二	星期三	星期四	星期五
上午		中文	英语	数学	地理	数学
		数学	数学	中文	数学	中文
		英语	中文	英语	历史	英语
下午		地理	历史		英语	历史
			地理		中文	

_____   _____

1. State what subjects these pictures represent.

 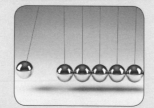  

2. Tell your Chinese friend the courses you have this year and specifically today. Then ask which courses he/she has this year and specifically today.

3. Today is Tuesday. There is a new student in class. Tell him the classes he'll have tomorrow based on the schedule below.

Class Schedule					
	星期一	星期二	星期三	星期四	星期五
第一节	数学	物理	数学	化学	物理
第二节	中文	化学	中文	数学	美术
第三节	物理	美术	物理	物理	化学
第四节	化学	数学	美术	中文	中文
第五节	美术	中文	化学	美术	美术

4. Here is a list of course options for next year. Tell your teacher what courses you have had and what courses you haven't had.

Course list	
1) 英语	6) 物理
2) 数学	7) 化学
3) 中文	8) 生物
4) 化学	9) 美术
5) 音乐	

1. Read Tianming's report card from last term and list the subjects he is especially good at.

科目	历史	数学	英语	中文	体育
Tianming's Report Card					
成绩	A	B	A+	B+	A+

_____

2. Read the following paragraph of Xiaowei's weekly schedule. Determine whether the following statements are true (T) or false (F).

小伟今年有五门课，英语、数学、美术、生物和物理。星期一有英语、美术、生物和物理。星期二有英语、数学、生物和物理。星期三有数学、美术、生物和物理。星期四有英语、数学、美术和生物。星期五五门课都有。

1) 小伟星期一没有美术。 （　　）

2) 小伟星期二有英语、数学、美术和物理。 （　　）

3) 小伟星期三有数学、美术、生物和物理。 （　　）

4) 小伟星期四没有物理。 （　　）

5) 小伟星期五有英语、数学、美术、生物和物理。 （　　）

3. The Guidance Department in your school has created a questionnaire for all new students. Answer the questions based on your personal situation.

1) 今年你有几门课？

Ⓐ 五门　　　　Ⓑ 六门　　　　Ⓒ 七门　　　　Ⓓ 八门　　　　（　　）

2) 你学过什么课？ / 你学过哪门课？

Ⓐ 中文　　　　Ⓑ 数学　　　　Ⓒ 物理　　　　Ⓓ 地理　　　　（　　）

1. Practice writing the following characters in the correct stroke order.

课 课 课 课 课 课 课 课 课 课

课

门 门 门

门

过 过 过 过 过 过

过

英 英 英 英 英 英 英 英

英

语 语 语 语 语 语 语 语 语

语

数 数 数 数 数 数 数 数 数 数 数 数 数

数

美 美 美 美 美 美 美 美 美

美

术

术 术 术 术 术

术	术	术					

音

音 音 音 音 音 音 音 音 音

音	音	音					

乐

乐 乐 乐 乐 乐

乐	乐	乐					

物

物 物 物 物 物 物 物 物

物	物	物					

体

体 体 体 体 体 体 体

体	体	体					

育

育 育 育 育 育 育 育 育

育	育	育					

2. Change the following sentences into questions that ask for the underlined content.

1) 我有四门课。

_____

2) 我学过数学。

_____

3) 今年我有数学课、英语课、中文课、音乐课和美术课。

_____

4) 学校里有体育馆和教学楼。

_____

5) 墙上有一张中国地图。

_____

3. Write your weekly classes for this term in the following schedule.

Weekly Schedule					
	星期一	星期二	星期三	星期四	星期五
第一节					
第二节					
第三节					
第四节					
第五节					
第六节					

4. Respond to your Chinese pen pal's e-mail based on your personal family's situation and your schedule.

_____同学，

　　你好！

　　很高兴做你的笔友。我叫小伟，今年十五岁，是北京第四中学的学生。今年我上八年级。我家有三口人，爸爸、妈妈都是老师。我们还有一只狗，叫 Harry。我很喜欢它。我们的学校很大，有三个教学楼、一个图书馆和一个体育馆。今年我有八门课，中文、数学、英语、生物、化学、物理、体育和美术。我最喜欢生物。明年我没有美术课，有音乐课。美术课和音乐课我都喜欢。你呢？你有几门课？是什么课？你最喜欢什么课？

　　祝好！

　　　　　　　　　　　　　　　　小伟
　　　　　　　　　　　　　　　　2012年7月10日

My busy schedule

STEP 1 ABOUT ONE'S CLASS SCHEDULE

Listening

1. Listening rejoinder. Choose the correct response.

    Ⓐ 五节课。

    Ⓑ 今天星期一。

    Ⓒ 我家离学校不远。

    Ⓓ 我们在教室上课。   (   )

2. Listening rejoinder. Choose the correct response.

    Ⓐ 八点上课，十二点下课。   Ⓑ 一点上课，三点下课。

    Ⓒ 八点上课，三点下课。   Ⓓ 九点上课，十二点下课。   (   )

3. You and Tom have English and history classes together. Tom sent you
    a voice mail about his class schedule on Monday morning. Listen to
    Tom's message and answer the question. (Imagine that you are Toby.)

    QUESTION: Are both of you going to meet on Monday morning in class?

    _____.

4. Mike is talking about his class schedule today. Listen and figure out what day
    it is today.

星期一	星期二	星期三	星期四	星期五
电脑	英语	中文	数学	中文
历史	数学	英语	中文	数学
英语	电脑	电脑	历史	历史
中文	历史	体育	英语	电脑
午饭				
体育	中文			

_____

1. You want your friend to give you a ride on Monday morning. In order to make sure you both have the same starting time, what questions do you need to ask?

2. You are hosting a visiting student on Tuesday, and this student will go with you to your classes. Tell your schedule based on your personal life.

3. You are doing a survey among students to determine the total number and type of classes they have on Friday. What questions should you ask?

4. You are a volunteer tutor. You need to know which day your student has Chinese class so that you can help with the homework. What question do you ask to find out this information?

Reading ✧

1. Mary has received a message from Kate:

   我今天第三节课是数学课，借我一把尺子，行吗？

   Look at Mary's schedule and decide if she can lend her ruler to Kate.

   Mary 今天的课：中文，英语，数学，物理，美术，历史。

   A Yes　　　　**B** No　　　　(　　)

2. Mary sends her father a message. When should Mary's father come to pick her up?
   A 12:00 pm　　**B** 2:00 pm
   C 1:00 pm　　**D** 3:00 pm　　(　　)

   > New Message　　　　Cancel
   > To: 爸爸
   > 我今天有五节课，下午两点放学。

3. Choose the correct answer to complete the short conversational exchange.

   1) a: _____?
      b: 我今天有中文课。

   A 你今天几节课？　　　　**B** 你今天有什么课？
   C 你今天几点上中文课？　　**D** 你在哪儿上中文课？　　　(　　)

2) a: _____?

b: 我八点上课，八点四十五分下课。

Ⓐ 今天你有中文课吗？　　Ⓑ 你上几节课？

Ⓒ 你从几点到几点上学？　　Ⓓ 你几点上课，几点下课？　　　（　　）

4.　Read Xiaoli's schedule and answer the questions.

Schedule					
	星期一	星期二	星期三	星期四	星期五
第一节	数学	物理	数学	化学	物理
第二节	中文	化学	中文	数学	英语
第三节	物理	英语	英语	物理	化学
第四节	化学	数学	美术	英语	中文
午休 (12:00 – 1:00 pm)					
第五节	美术	中文	化学	美术	美术
第六节	英语	美术	物理	中文	数学

1) 小丽星期三有几节课？

_____

2) 星期二上午她有什么课？

_____

3) 星期四的第一节课几点上课，
几点下课？ (School starts at 8:00 am,
and each period lasts 45 minutes)

_____

4) 她一个星期有几节中文课？

_____

 Writing

1.　Practice writing the following characters in the correct stroke order.

节 节 节 节 节

节

放 放 放 放 放 放 放 放

放

2. Jerry needs a ride home after school. Text him to let him know the time you finish school today based on your personal life.

3. Michael texts you asking what classes you are having today. Reply to him based on your personal life.

4. Write a paragraph of how many classes you have on Monday mornings, what they are, and when the first class starts and ends.

_____

_____

_____

MORE ABOUT ONE'S CLASS SCHEDULE

Listening

1. Listening rejoinder. Choose the correct response.

   (A) 十一点。   (B) 十点。

   (C) 从十一点到十一点五十分。 (D) 十二点。   (   )

2. Annie is talking about her Tuesday schedule. Listen and choose the correct answer to the question.

   QUESTION: What is Annie's second class?

   (A) 数学   (B) 物理   (C) 生物   (D) 英语   (   )

3. Listening rejoinder. Choose the correct response.

   (A) 三点以后我在学校。   (B) 三点以前我有中文课。

   (C) 我三点下课。   (D) 三点以后我没有课。   (   )

4. You plan to visit Lily's Chinese class on Tuesday morning. She is telling you her class schedule for Tuesday morning. Fill in the blanks and circle the time slot you will be in her class.

Tuesday			
第一节 8:00 – 8:50	第二节 9:00 – 9:50	第三节 10:00 – 10:50	第四节 11:00 – 11:50
		数学	体育

Speaking

1. In China, students go to school from Monday to Friday. What about students in the United States? From what day to what day do you go to school?

2. Lily's school starts at 8:30 am and ends at 3:30 pm on Monday. From what time to what time do you have school on Monday?

3. Xiaocheng is asking his classmate what the classes are before and after 9 a.m. today. What should he say?

1. Choose the correct answer to the question.

   QUESTION: 明天从下午一点到两点你有什么课？　　　　　　　(　)

   Ⓐ 明天我有一节中文课。

   Ⓑ 明天下午我有中文课。

   Ⓒ 明天下午的中文课有四十五分钟。

   Ⓓ 明天从下午一点到两点我有中文课。

2. Choose the correct question for the answer.

   QUESTION: _____?　　　　　　　(　)

   ANSWER: 我三点以前上中文课，三点以后没有课。

   Ⓐ 你三点放学吗？

   Ⓑ 你三点以前做什么？

   Ⓒ 你三点以后做什么？

   Ⓓ 你三点以前是什么课？三点以后是什么课？

3. Read Mary's schedule and answer the following questions.

	星期一	星期二	星期三	星期四	星期五
第一节	电脑	英语	中文	数学	中文
第二节	历史	数学	英语	中文	数学
第三节	英语	电脑	电脑	历史	历史
第四节	中文	历史	体育	英语	电脑
午休 (12:00 – 1:00 pm)					
第五节	体育	中文			
第六节					

1) Mary 一个星期有几节中文课？

   Ⓐ 四　　　　Ⓑ 三　　　　Ⓒ 五　　　　Ⓓ 二　　　　(　)

2) 她星期三有几节课？

   Ⓐ 四　　　　Ⓑ 三　　　　Ⓒ 五　　　　Ⓓ 二　　　　(　)

3) 星期四上午她上什么课?

Ⓐ 中文、数学、历史、电脑　　Ⓑ 中文、数学、历史、英文

Ⓒ 中文、数学、电脑、体育　　Ⓓ 数学、中文、历史、英文（　　）

4) 星期一她从上学到放学，有多少节课?

Ⓐ 三　　　　Ⓑ 四　　　　Ⓒ 五　　　　Ⓓ 六　　　　（　　）

5) 星期五电脑课以前是什么课?

Ⓐ 数学　　　Ⓑ 历史　　　Ⓒ 体育　　　Ⓓ 物理　　　（　　）

Writing

1. Practice writing the following characters in the correct stroke order.

以 以 以 以

前 前 前 前 前 前 前 前 前

| 以前 | 以前 | 以前 | | |

以 以 以 以

后 后 后 后 后 后

| 以后 | 以后 | 以后 | | |

从 从 从 从

| 从 | 从 | 从 | 从 | | | | |

到 到 到 到 到 到 到 到

| 到 | 到 | 到 | | | | | |

2. Fill in the blanks with the following words: 以前, 以后, 从, 到.

1) 上学＿＿＿＿＿我在家里，上学＿＿＿＿＿我在学校。

2) 放学＿＿＿＿＿我在学校，放学＿＿＿＿＿我在家里。

3) ＿＿＿＿＿五岁＿＿＿＿＿十岁我在小学上学。
   elementary school

4) 十三岁＿＿＿＿＿我在高中上学。
   gāo
   high school

5) ＿＿＿＿＿十二月二十号＿＿＿＿＿一月二号，我们不上课。

3. Write a reply to the following e-mail.

＿＿＿＿＿同学，

　　你好！

　　在中国，我们从三月一号到六月三十号上学。七月和八月不上学。从九月一号到一月三十一号上学。二月不上学。从星期一到星期五上学。星期六和星期日不上学。

　　在美国，学生从几月到几月上学？从几月到几月不上学？

祝好！

　　　　　　　　　　小成

　　　　　　　　　　二〇一一年九月一日

_____

_____

_____

_____

_____

STEP 3 ABOUT ONE'S DAILY SCHEDULE

Listening 🎧

1. Listening rejoinder. Choose the correct response.

    Ⓐ 我吃早饭。

    Ⓑ 我早上八点打球。

    Ⓒ 我早上七点起床。

    Ⓓ 起床以后我吃饭。

    (   )

2. Listening rejoinder. Choose the correct response.

    Ⓐ 我昨天没看电视。

    Ⓑ 我昨天看电视了。

    Ⓒ 我明天去北京。

    Ⓓ 我今天有中文课。

    (   )

3. Your teacher is introducing a Chinese film that will be shown in the auditorium of your school campus. Listen and check your schedule to see if you can go.

    Your schedule:

Mon	Tue	Wed	Thu	Fri
AM: Classes	AM: Classes	AM: Classes	AM: Classes	AM: Classes
PM: Sports	PM: Available	PM: 1:00–3:00 Internet 3:00–5:00 Homework	PM: Available	PM: Available

    Ⓐ Yes   Ⓑ No

    (   )

146

4. Mary is talking about her Saturday schedule. Listen and choose the correct order of activities.

    A 做功课 – 打球 – 吃午饭   **B** 吃午饭 – 打球 – 做功课

    C 打球 – 吃午饭 – 做功课   **D** 做功课 – 吃午饭 – 打球   (   )

Speaking

1. What do you usually do after having dinner and until going to bed on weekdays? (Based on your personal schedule)

2. You are with a host family in Beijing. They ask you about the time you eat your three meals. Tell when you usually have breakfast, lunch, and dinner on weekdays in the United States in three sentences.

3. Talk about three special weekend activities you did last weekend in three sentences including where you did it.

4. Which room is your favorite room in your home? What can you do there? When is the most recent time that you used that room and what did you do there?

Reading

1. The following is Mike's daily routine. Match the activities with the most logical time and place.

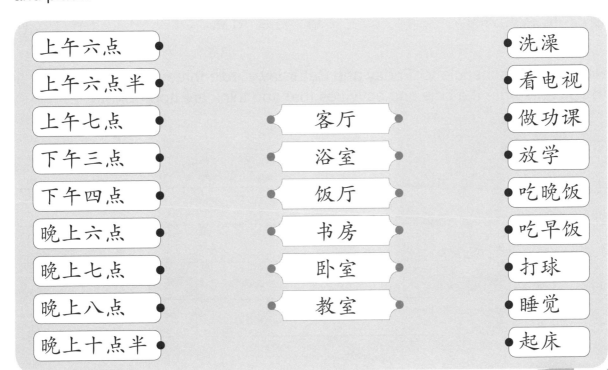

上午六点   客厅   洗澡
上午六点半   看电视
上午七点   浴室   做功课
下午三点   饭厅   放学
下午四点   书房   吃晚饭
晚上六点   吃早饭
晚上七点   卧室   打球
晚上八点   教室   睡觉
晚上十点半   起床

2. Lily wants to include the three activities on the right into her daily schedule on the left. Read the schedule to see if there are available time slots for these activities. Then write the time slots beside each activity.

Lily's Daily Schedule	
6:00 am	起床
7:00 am	早饭
8:00 am – 12:00 pm	上课
12:00 pm – 1:00 pm	午饭
1:00 pm – 3:00 pm	上课
5:00 pm – 6:00 pm	晚饭
10:00 pm	睡觉

1) 打球：_____

2) 洗澡：_____

3) 做功课：_____

3. Fill in the blanks. Choose the question for the answer.

1) QUESTION: _____?
   ANSWER: 我在教室上中文课。

   Ⓐ 你今天有几节课？　　　　Ⓑ 你今天有什么课？
   Ⓒ 你今天几点上中文课？　　Ⓓ 你在哪里上中文课？　　（　　）

2) QUESTION: _____?
   ANSWER: 我早上八点起床。

   Ⓐ 你几点睡觉？　　　　　　Ⓑ 你起床了吗？
   Ⓒ 你几点起床？　　　　　　Ⓓ 现在几点？　　　　　　（　　）

4. Read Mark's schedule for Friday and Saturday. Circle three items that are not right to you and write the time and activities that you think are appropriate.

星期五	
3:00 pm	放学 _____
3:00 – 6:00 pm	打球 _____
7:00 pm	吃晚饭 _____
8:00 – 11:30 pm	上网 _____
11:50 pm	睡觉 _____

STEP UP WITH CHINESE

12:00 pm	起床	_____
12:30 pm	吃午饭	_____
1:00 pm – 4:00 pm	看电影	_____
5:00 pm	吃晚饭	_____
6:00 pm – 7:00 pm	看电视	_____
8:00 pm – 11:00 pm	做功课	_____

Writing

1. Practice writing the following characters in the correct stroke order.

起 起 起 起 起 起 起 起 起 起

床 床 床 床 床 床 床

起床 | 起床 | 起床 | | |

吃 吃 吃 吃 吃 吃

吃 | 吃 | 吃 | 吃 | | | | |

饭 饭 饭 饭 饭 饭 饭

饭 | 饭 | 饭 | 饭 | | | | |

做 做 做 做 做 做 做 做 做 做 做

做 | 做 | 做 | 做 | | | | |

看 看看看看看看看看看

看 | 看 | 看 | 看 | | | | |

睡 睡睡睡睡睡睡睡睡睡睡睡睡睡

睡 | 睡 | 睡 | 睡 | | | | |

厅 厅厅厅厅

厅 | 厅 | 厅 | 厅 | | | | |

房 房房房房房房房房

房 | 房 | 房 | 房 | | | | |

上 上 上
网 网网网网网网

上网 | 上网 | 上网 | | |

聊 聊聊聊聊聊聊聊聊聊聊聊
天 天 天 天

聊天 | 聊天 | 聊天 | | |

2.   Write in Chinese the activities usually done in these rooms.

卧室：_____

浴室：_____

餐厅：_____

客厅：_____

书房：_____

3. Answer the following questions based on your personal life.

1) 你今天早上几点起床？

_____

2) 起床以后你做什么了？

_____

3) 今天你几点吃早饭？

_____

4) 早饭以后你做什么了？

_____

5) 今天上午你有几节课？是什么课？

_____

6) 从九点到十点你有什么课？

_____

7) 你今天几点放学？

_____

8) 放学以后，你做什么？

_____

4. Write three activities that you want to put into your daily schedule. Indicate the time you would like to do these things using 以前 and 以后.

_____

_____

_____

My interests, my dreams

STEP 1 ABOUT ONE'S INTERESTS AND HOBBIES

Listening

1. Mary is talking about her hobbies. Listen and find the one that she <u>did not</u> mention.

   Ⓐ 滑雪　　　Ⓑ 跑步　　　Ⓒ 登山　　　Ⓓ 画画儿　　　(　　)

2. Listening rejoinder. Choose the correct response.

   Ⓐ 我的爱好是游泳。　　　Ⓑ 我不是学生。

   Ⓒ 我喜欢绿色。　　　Ⓓ 我妹妹的爱好是看书。　　　(　　)

3. Mary and Jerry are talking about their hobbies. Listen and decide which sport they can do together.

   Ⓐ 登山　　　Ⓑ 滑雪　　　Ⓒ 跳舞　　　Ⓓ 看书　　　(　　)

4. Lisa and her twin sister Sara have very different hobbies. Lisa is an outdoor activity lover while Sara prefers the indoors. Listen and decide who Lisa is and who Sara is.

   The first speaker is _____.

   The second speaker is _____

Speaking

1. Look at the pictures below and introduce two of Tom's hobbies.

2. You have just made a new friend and want to know about his/her interests and hobbies. What do you say? What questions can you ask?

3.   Talk about and describe your best friend's interests and hobbies.

4.   You are to choose a sport to play for this term. Tell your teacher your interests.

Reading

1.   Match the people with similar hobbies and write down the common hobbies for each pair.

Mark	Brian	Zach	Daniel
踢足球，打篮球，橄榄球，棒球	游泳，打乒乓球，下棋，画画儿	打网球，跳舞，唱歌	读书，登山，弹钢琴

Ruth	Mia	Anna	Martha
游泳，画画儿	唱歌，跳舞	登山，弹钢琴	踢足球，打篮球

1) _____

2) _____

3) _____

4) _____

2. The school is going on a field trip to a writing workshop. Read the dialog and see who will go, Rita or Josh?

_____.

> Rita ： Josh，你喜欢读书吗？
> Josh ： 对，我很喜欢读书，也喜欢写作。你的爱好是什么？
> Rita ： 我的爱好是唱歌。我不喜欢写作。

3. Your class is looking for a helper for the P.E. teacher. The person should have interests in many sports and love to participate in sports with others. Here is Jim's application. Do you think he is the right person for the job?

_____.

> 我是Jim。我有很多体育爱好。上中学以前，我学过五年足球和篮球。上中学以后，我学过乒乓球、网球，还学过羽毛球。我很喜欢体育，最喜欢和同学们打球。

4. Your class is organizing a cheering squad. Based on the hobbies and interests, who do you think would be interested in leading it?

Emmy	Joan	Jenny	Nicole	Ashley	Mickie
看橄榄球	弹钢琴	打太极拳	跳舞	唱歌	滑雪

Writing

1. Practice writing the following characters in the correct stroke order.

爱好

爱好	爱好		

跑 跑 跑 跑 跑 跑 跑 跑 跑 跑 跑
步 步 步 步 步 步 步

跑步

跑步	跑步		

游 游 游 游 游 游 游 游 游 游 游
泳 泳 泳 泳 泳 泳 泳 泳

游泳

游泳	游泳		

篮 篮 篮 篮 篮 篮 篮 篮 篮 篮 篮 篮 篮 篮 篮
球 球 球 球 球 球 球 球 球 球 球

篮球

篮球	篮球		

唱 唱 唱 唱 唱 唱 唱 唱 唱 唱
歌 歌 歌 歌 歌 歌 歌 歌 歌 歌 歌 歌 歌

唱歌

唱歌	唱歌		

跳 跳 跳 跳 跳 跳 跳 跳 跳 跳 跳 跳
舞 舞 舞 舞 舞 舞 舞 舞 舞 舞 舞 舞 舞 舞

跳舞

跳舞	跳舞		

2. Fill in the blanks with questions or answers that are logically part of the dialog.

A：你有篮球吗？

B：我没有，_____。你喜欢打篮球吗？

A：对，我喜欢打篮球。你的爱好是什么？

B：_____。

A：我的爱好也是游泳。

3. Put the following form into a paragraph that talks about a family's interests and hobbies.

爸爸	妈妈	哥哥	Lily
下棋，写书法，打太极拳	游泳，画画儿，看书，写作	打棒球，登山，滑雪	弹钢琴，唱歌，跳舞

_____

_____

_____

_____

4. Talk about two of your hobbies and ask your classmates two questions about their interests and hobbies.

_____

_____

_____

_____

STEP 2 ABOUT ONE'S ABILITIES AND SKILLS

Listening

1. Listening rejoinder. Choose the correct response.

   Ⓐ 我的妹妹会打网球。　　　Ⓑ 我不会。

   Ⓒ 你在哪里打网球？　　　　Ⓓ 打网球的人很多。　　　（　　）

2. Listening rejoinder. Choose the correct response.

   Ⓐ 她打过篮球。　　　　　　Ⓑ 她去年学过打篮球。

   Ⓒ 她打篮球打得很好。　　　Ⓓ 她今年不打篮球。　　　（　　）

3. Lily is talking with Tom.

   QUESTION: What sport can they play together?

   Ⓐ 游泳　　　　Ⓑ 登山　　　　Ⓒ 乒乓球　　　　Ⓓ 羽毛球　　（　　）

4. Listen to the dialog between Lily and Mary and find out who swims the fastest.

   Ⓐ Lily　　　　Ⓑ Mary　　　　Ⓒ Tom　　　　Ⓓ Mary 的弟弟　（　　）

Speaking

1. Your family is going to participate in a family weekend sport competition. You need to tell the organizer the sports your family members are good at. Use 得 and explain to the organizer about your family and the sports each person likes to play and is good at playing.

2. Your friend Henry is looking for a piano tutor. Mary is very good at piano playing. How do you recommend Mary to Henry? Describe her abilities.

3. Your class is going to perform *Taiji* at a lunar festival party. You want to know your teacher's comments after the rehearsal. What kind of questions can you ask?

4. Pick one art and one sport from the list on the right, talk about your interests, and how well you do them.

体育	篮球	跑步	游泳
弹钢琴	跳舞	唱歌	画画儿

1. Read the following form and mark "T" if the statement is true and "F" if the statement is false.

	Lucy	Jack	小成	芳芳	天明
爱好	打太极拳	写书法	打网球	看书	滑雪
tècháng 特长 strength	游泳	打太极拳	弹钢琴	写作	打乒乓球

1) Lucy喜欢打太极拳。她游泳游得很慢。 ( )
2) Jack的爱好是写书法。他打太极拳打得很好。 ( )
3) 小成不喜欢打网球。他弹钢琴弹得很好。 ( )
4) 芳芳的爱好是看书。她写作写得很好。 ( )
5) 天明喜欢滑雪。他打乒乓球打得很好。 ( )

2. Put in the correct names of the animals for the descriptions given.
( ) 飞得很快。
( ) 没有手，游泳游得很快。
( ) 四条腿，跑得很快。
( ) 没有腿，爬得很快。
( ) 不大，跳得很快。
( ) 很胖，很喜欢睡觉。

Ⓐ 马　　Ⓑ 鱼　　Ⓒ 鸟
Ⓓ 兔子　Ⓔ 蛇　　Ⓕ 猪

3. Mark "T" if the statement is true and "F" if the statement is false.
1) 很多中国人会打乒乓球，很多美国人不会打乒乓球。 ( )
2) 很多美国人喜欢打橄榄球，很多中国人不太喜欢打橄榄球。 ( )
3) 很多美国人不会打太极拳，很多中国老人会打太极拳。 ( )
4) 很多美国人的爱好是写书法，很多中国人的爱好是打棒球。 ( )

4. Put a check for those activities that you can do and a cross for those you cannot do.
( ) 游泳　　　　( ) 滑雪　　　　( ) 打太极拳
( ) 踢足球　　　( ) 写书法　　　( ) 登山
( ) 打羽毛球　　( ) 下棋　　　　( ) 打橄榄球
( ) 打棒球　　　( ) 打乒乓球　　( ) 跳舞

1. Practice writing the following characters in the correct stroke order.

得 得 得 得 得 得 得 得 得 得 得

得 | 得 | 得 | 得 | | | | |

快 快 快 快 快 快 快

快 | 快 | 快 | 快 | | | | |

慢 慢 慢 慢 慢 慢 慢 慢 慢 慢 慢 慢 慢 慢

慢 | 慢 | 慢 | 慢 | | | | |

怎 怎 怎 怎 怎 怎 怎 怎 怎

怎 | 怎 | 怎 | 怎 | | | | |

2. List in Chinese all of the sports you can play or have played. Then put a check after those sports that you are good at.

_____

_____

_____

3. Write a sentence for each of the following people on what he/she can do and how well he/she does it.

Example: Michael Jackson；他会唱歌。他唱歌唱得很好。

a) Michael Jordan _____

b) The Williams Sisters _____

c) David Beckham _____

d) Vincent Van Gogh _____

e) Lady Gaga _____

f) Babe Ruth _____

g) Natalie Portman _____

h) Michael Phelps _____

i) Peyton Manning _____

j) Louisa May Alcott _____

4. Xiao Wang observed that the following sports are very popular in the U.S. and China. Write two sentences to describe it.

America — baseball and soccer

China — badminton and ping pong

_____

_____

_____

_____

_____

Listening

1. Listening rejoinder. Choose the correct response.

   Ⓐ 我是玛丽。　　　　　Ⓑ 我早上七点起床。

   Ⓒ 我喜欢唱歌。　　　　Ⓓ 我喜欢跳舞，将来想当舞蹈家。　（　　　）

2. Listening rejoinder. Choose the correct response.

   Ⓐ 他打篮球打得很好。　　Ⓑ 他喜欢音乐。

   Ⓒ 对，他想当歌手。　　　Ⓓ 他的爱好是唱歌。　（　　　）

3. Ms. Li is talking about her students' interests. Listen and match students with their future dreams.

   1) Lily ●　　　　　　● 钢琴家

   2) Mark ●　　　　　　● 画家

   3) 李英 ●　　　　　　● 作家

   4) 王朋 ●　　　　　　● 舞蹈家

   5) 张小美 ●　　　　　　● 运动员

4. The four traditional Chinese hobbies are: 琴 (弹琴), 棋 (下棋), 书 (写书法), 画 (画画). Listen and match the four famous Chinese people with their specialties by putting A, B, C, or D next to the right hobby.

   Qǐ Gōng
   Ⓐ 启功

   Qí Báishí
   Ⓑ 齐白石

   Láng Lǎng
   Ⓒ 郎朗

   Niè Wèipíng
   Ⓓ 聂卫平

   琴：＿＿＿＿＿＿＿＿　　棋：＿＿＿＿＿＿＿＿

   书：＿＿＿＿＿＿＿＿　　画：＿＿＿＿＿＿＿＿

1. The following pictures are activities Wang Xiaodong and friends do every day. Prepare a brief introduction of everyone. Follow the example below.

Example: Lucy 天天跳舞。她想当舞蹈家。

A Mary   **B** Wang Xiaodong   **C** Mark   **D** Michelle

2. Carol and her siblings are all good at sports. Talk about her brothers and sister using the following sentence as an example.

Example:
Carol 会打篮球。她将来想当篮球运动员。

A John   **B** Louise   **C** Mike

3. Answer the following questions based on your life.
   1) What is your hobby?
   2) What is your best friend's hobby?
   3) Do you play soccer? How well can you play soccer?
   4) Do you know how to swim? Do you swim fast?
   5) What do you want to do in the future?
   6) I run every day, do you?

4. Look at the following pictures and tell what professions the people represent. Is there anyone among them you like? Are there any professions that you are personally considering?

1. A group of visiting students from China need to find their host students in your school. Match the students according to similar hobbies.

Visiting Students	Host Students
1) Mark 喜欢踢足球、打篮球。	王成喜欢打羽毛球和登山。
2) Cindy 的爱好是打太极拳和滑雪。	李丽的爱好是弹钢琴和唱歌。
3) John 打乒乓球打得很好，画画儿也画得很好。	张小英每天都跑步，她会打网球和乒乓球。
4) Mike 喜欢打羽毛球，唱歌也唱得很好。	芳芳打太极拳打得很好，也会弹钢琴。
5) Brian 每天弹钢琴，将来想当钢琴家。	张小棋喜欢下棋，爱好踢足球。

2. The following paragraph is about everyone's hobbies. Put each person into groups based on the three sports below.

　　我和我的同学都很喜欢体育。Mark 和 Mike 喜欢踢足球和打橄榄球。John 和 Jack 喜欢游泳和滑雪。Mary 喜欢登山和滑雪。Brian 打棒球打得很好，他也喜欢游泳。我喜欢打太极拳，也喜欢打棒球和网球。

橄榄球：_____

滑雪：_____

棒球：_____

3. Read the following dialog and match the people with their future dreams.

> Mary：你喜欢游泳吗？
>
> Ben ：我很喜欢游泳，我也喜欢踢足球。你呢？
>
> Mary：我不喜欢踢足球，我喜欢看足球。我的爱好是打网球，我很喜欢 Williams 姐妹。
>
> Ben ：她们打网球打得很好，很多人喜欢她们。你将来想当网球运动员吗？
>
> Mary：不，我想当教师。你呢？
>
> Ben ：我很喜欢游泳，我想当游泳运动员，我喜欢 Michael Phelps。

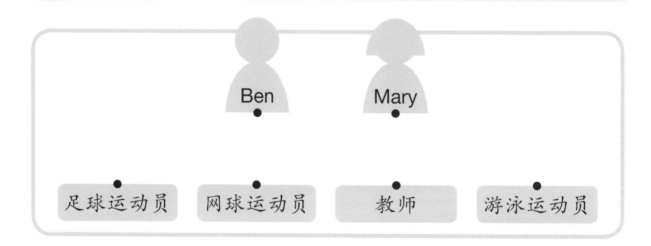

	Ben	Mary	
足球运动员	网球运动员	教师	游泳运动员

4. Here are the sports that Mark's school offers. Which ones does your school also offer? Make a list of the sports that both schools have in common.

Sports in Mark's school				
足球	篮球	橄榄球	páiqiú 排球 volleyball	网球
滑雪	bīngqiú 冰球 ice hockey	chǎngpǎo 长跑 long-distance running	棒球	lěiqiú 垒球 softball

1. Practice writing the following characters in the correct stroke order.

将 将 将 将 将 将 将 将 将

来 来 来 来 来 来 来

将来 | 将来 | 将来 | |

想 想 想 想 想 想 想 想 想 想 想 想

想 | 想 | 想 | 想 | | | | |

当 当 当 当 当 当

当 | 当 | 当 | 当 | | | |

每 每 每 每 每 每 每

每 | 每 | 每 | 每 | | | |

2. Write at least three sports that you can play and how well you play them. If you do not play any sports or like to play any sports, then write three sports that one of your friend plays.

   Example: 我会打篮球。我打篮球打得很好。

3. The following pictures are the Brown's family hobbies. Write one sentence introducing each of Michael and Michelle's hobbies and another sentence telling the children's future professional plans.

Michael

Michelle

1) Michael _____。 他 _____。

2) Michelle_____。 她 _____。

4. Read the following e-mail from your Chinese pen pal. Write your pen pal an e-mail reply that addresses some of the same information.

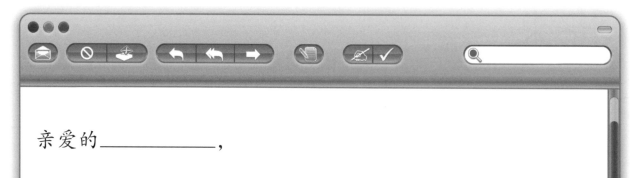

亲爱的_____，

你好！

我是北京第四中学的学生，今年十年级。我有五门课，数学、语文、英语、历史和体育。我每天七点起床，八点上课。我下午五点放学。从八点到十点，我做功课。我的功课很多，每天都很忙。

我喜欢游泳，也喜欢打羽毛球。我最喜欢唱歌。天天都唱。我将来想当歌手。我的家人都喜欢体育。我爸爸的爱好是打篮球。我妈妈每天早上打太极拳。星期六我们一家人打羽毛球。

你的学校怎么样？你有什么爱好？

祝好！

王小丽

二〇一二年十月五日

LESSON 10 It tastes so good!

STEP 1 TALKING ABOUT FOODS AND HOW THEY TASTE

Listening

1. Listen to a dialog in a restaurant and answer the question.
   QUESTION: Is this a Chinese restaurant or a Western restaurant?

   _____.

2. Listening rejoinder. Choose the correct response.
   Ⓐ 我吃炒饭
   Ⓑ 我吃饺子。
   Ⓒ 我吃面包。
   Ⓓ 我喝茶。   (   )

3. Listening rejoinder. Choose the correct response.
   Ⓐ 我喜欢面条。
   Ⓑ 我的炒饭很好吃。
   Ⓒ 我的汤很好喝。
   Ⓓ 我吃饺子。   (   )

4. Listen and choose the correct answer to the question.
   QUESTION: What does Tom want to drink?
   Ⓐ Tea   Ⓑ Coke   Ⓒ Juice   Ⓓ Coffee   (   )

Speaking

1. You are in a Chinese restaurant with an American friend. Ask your friend if the dumplings and tea are good.

2. Describe food and drinks that have one of these tastes: sour, sweet, bitter, spicy, salty.

   Example: 茶很苦。

3. You are hosting a Chinese student in your home for this term. You want to know what he/she eats and drinks for breakfast. What questions would you ask?

1. Rita is in a Chinese restaurant for lunch. She is a vegetarian. She likes sweet and bland food, but does not like spicy or bitter food. Read the following menu and order a Chinese dish and drink for her. Mark a "✔" by the items you choose.

☐ 素炒面 — ¥10.00
vegetarian fried noodles

☐ 糖醋排骨 — ¥20.00
sweet and sour pork

☐ 宫保鸡丁 — ¥15.00
spicy chicken

☐ 麻婆豆腐 — ¥ 8.00
spicy beancurd

☐ 红豆汤 — ¥ 2.00
red bean soup

☐ 中国茶 — ¥ 1.00
Chinese tea

2. Read the description of a food and guess what it is.

它很好吃。它有面包、生菜、番茄、奶酪和肉。人们喜欢喝可乐，吃炸薯条和它。它是什么？

Ⓐ 咖啡
Ⓑ 披萨
Ⓒ 饺子
Ⓓ 汉堡   (   )

3. Mary has just arrived in China and is very interested in Chinese food. However, she does not eat meat or fish. What do you suggest she have for breakfast? Circle the items she would most likely order.

Food

牛肉面　肉包子　油条　面包

Drinks

咖啡　茶　牛奶　果汁　豆浆

馄饨汤　鸡肉粥　鱼粥

1. Practice writing the following characters in the correct stroke order.

吃 吃 吃 吃 吃 吃

吃 | 吃 | 吃 | 吃 | | | | |

喝 喝 喝 喝 喝 喝 喝 喝 喝 喝 喝 喝

喝 | 喝 | 喝 | 喝 | | | | |

酸 酸 酸 酸 酸 酸 酸 酸 酸 酸 酸 酸 酸 酸

酸 | 酸 | 酸 | 酸 | | | | |

甜 甜 甜 甜 甜 甜 甜 甜 甜 甜 甜

甜 | 甜 | 甜 | 甜 | | | | |

苦 苦 苦 苦 苦 苦 苦 苦

苦 | 苦 | 苦 | 苦 | | | | |

辣 辣 辣 辣 辣 辣 辣 辣 辣 辣 辣 辣 辣 辣

辣 | 辣 | 辣 | 辣 | | | | |

淡 淡 淡 淡 淡 淡 淡 淡 淡 淡 淡

淡 | 淡 | 淡 | 淡 | | | | |

2. Write a short commentary on pizza and coke. Are they tasty? Do you like them?

_____

_____

_____

_____

_____

3. Guess the taste of the following Chinese dishes.

麻婆豆腐：　_____
spicy beancurd

酸辣汤：　　_____
hot and sour soup

芝麻汤圆：　_____
dumpling with
sesame filling

4. Make up your favorite Chinese menu below.

Menu

Staples	Dishes	Drinks
1) _____	1) _____	1) _____
2) _____	2) _____	2) _____
3) _____	3) _____	3) _____
4) _____	4) _____	4) _____

STEP 2 EXPRESSING FOOD PREFERENCES

Listening

1. Listening rejoinder. Choose the correct response.

   Ⓐ 我每天吃面包。　　Ⓑ 我喜欢喝可乐。

   Ⓒ 我不喜欢吃油条。　　Ⓓ 我喜欢吃炒面，也喜欢吃炒饭。 (　　)

2. Mary is talking about Chinese food. Listen and mark a "✔" for the foods she likes and a "✘" for those she dislikes.

   Ⓐ 饺子　　Ⓑ 包子　　Ⓒ 面包　　Ⓓ 热狗

3. Listen to the dialog and choose the foods that the person wanted.

   Ⓐ 炒饭，可乐　　Ⓑ 炒面，茶

   Ⓒ 白饭，可乐　　Ⓓ 炒饭，果汁 (　　)

4. Listen to the dialog and choose the food that the person wanted.

   Ⓐ 酸辣汤 suānlàtāng hot and sour soup　　Ⓑ 馄饨汤 húntuntāng wanton soup　　Ⓒ 蛋花汤 dànhuātāng egg drop soup　　Ⓓ 豆浆 dòujiāng soybean drink (　　)

Speaking

1. Share with your classmates your favorite Chinese food and favorite American food, as well as your least favorite Chinese food and least favorite American food.

2. You are helping to collect what people want to eat and drink for your field trip to Chinatown. What questions do you need to ask?

3. You invite your friend for dinner, but all you know how to cook is fried noodles and fried rice. Also, you only have tea and coke in your refrigerator. How do you ask your friend to choose a dish and drink?

1. Read the food list and group them according to whether they are a Chinese food or a Western food.

1) 汉堡
burger

2) 红豆汤
red bean soup

3) 炸薯条
French fries

4) 宫保鸡丁
spicy chicken

5) 牛排
steak

6) 冰淇淋
ice cream

7) 蛋炒饭
fried rice with egg

8) 绿茶
green tea

9) 可乐
coke

10) 麻婆豆腐
spicy beancurd

A. Chinese food：_____

_____

B. Western food：_____

_____

2. Fill in the blanks with the appropriate words below.

Ⓐ 还是　Ⓑ 吃　Ⓒ 喝　Ⓓ 最　Ⓔ 也

1) 我（　　　）喜欢吃中国菜。
2) 我要（　　　）牛奶，（　　　）面包。
3) 你们要吃中国菜，（　　　）美国菜？
4) 我喜欢吃汉堡，（　　　）喜欢吃炒面。

3. Choose the correct answers to the questions.
QUESTIONS:
1) 你吃什么？　　　　　（　　　）
2) 你喜欢吃饺子吗？　　（　　　）
3) 你要喝什么？　　　　（　　　）
4) 你要吃牛肉还是羊肉？（　　　）

Ⓐ 我吃炒面。
Ⓑ 羊肉，谢谢！
Ⓒ 喜欢！
Ⓓ 我要喝可乐。

1. Practice writing the following characters in the correct stroke order.

要 要 要 要 要 要 要 要 要

要 | 要 | 要 | 要 | | | | |

还 还 还 还 还 还 还
是 是 是 是 是 是 是 是 是

还是 | 还是 | 还是 | |

2. Your class is going to visit Chinatown and have lunch there. The teacher is collecting students' preferences for food and drink to place an order ahead of time. Write your favorite Chinese food and drink so that you can hand it in to the teacher.

_____

_____

_____

_____

3. Your class is going to celebrate the Chinese New Year. You are responsible for the menu. Write the dishes and drinks you plan to have.

Main dishes	Beverages

4. Write a description of American foods, including your favorite and least favorite ones. What do you often have for each meal? Describe the tastes of the foods that you like and dislike.

_____

_____

_____

_____

_____

STEP 3 ORDERING FOOD

Listening ✦

1. You and your friend are in a Chinese restaurant. Listen to her food preference and recommend a dish to her.

   Ⓐ 酸辣汤   Ⓑ 糖醋排骨   Ⓒ 宫保鸡丁   Ⓓ 麻婆豆腐   (   )
   hot and sour soup   sweet and sour pork   spicy chicken   spicy beancurd

2. Listening rejoinder. Choose the correct response.

   Ⓐ 我不喜欢吃汉堡。   Ⓑ 我不吃鱼。

   Ⓒ 你喝什么？   Ⓓ 我要一盘饺子。   (   )

3. Lily is telling the waiter what she has ordered. Listen and choose the correct receipt that belongs to Lily.

Receipt A	Receipt B	Receipt C
两个饺子	两个饺子	两个包子
一碗汤	一盘炒饭	一盘炒面
一杯可乐	一杯可乐	一杯可乐

   (   )

1. Below are pictures of what your five different friends want to order for drinks. Tell the waiter/waitress their choices.

2. You and your friend are in a Chinese restaurant. What do you say to your friend in order to find out his/her choice of food?

3. You are ordering food in a Chinese restaurant. Look at the menu and tell the waiter/waitress the food and drinks you would like.

Menu

Soup ($4)	suānlàtāng 酸辣汤 hot and sour soup	dànhuātāng 蛋花汤 egg drop soup	húntuntāng 馄饨汤 wanton soup
Main Course ($8)	Yángzhōuchǎofàn 扬州炒饭 Yangzhou fried rice	chǎomiàn 炒面 fried noodle	tángcùpáigǔ 糖醋排骨 sweet and sour pork
	gōngbǎojīdīng 宫保鸡丁 spicy chicken	mápódòufu 麻婆豆腐 spicy beancurd	

Drink ($2)	Zhōngguóchá 中国茶 Chinese tea	dòujiāng 豆浆 soybean drink	guǒzhī 果汁 fruit juice	kělè 可乐 coke

1. Read and choose the picture that the sentence describes.

桌子上有两块蛋糕和两杯咖啡。

A B (   )

2. Read the dialog between two friends. Write "T" if the statements are true and "F" if the statements are false.

小成：我喜欢吃汉堡，你呢？

小丽：我喜欢吃饺子。你喜欢吃饺子吗？

小成：我最喜欢吃饺子。我也喜欢吃汉堡和热狗。我不喜欢吃冰淇淋。

小丽：我最喜欢吃冰淇淋。我天天都吃！

1) 小成不喜欢吃饺子。 (   )
2) 小丽喜欢吃冰淇淋。 (   )
3) 小成和小丽都喜欢吃饺子。(   )

Writing

1. Practice writing the following characters in the correct stroke order.

碗 碗 碗 碗 碗 碗 碗 碗 碗 碗 碗 碗 碗

 碗 | 碗 | 碗 | 碗 | | | |

盘 盘 盘 盘 盘 盘 盘 盘 盘 盘 盘

盘

盘	盘	盘					

碟 碟 碟 碟 碟 碟 碟 碟 碟 碟 碟 碟 碟 碟

碟

碟	碟	碟					

份 份 份 份 份 份

份

份	份	份					

块 块 块 块 块 块 块

块

块	块	块					

杯 杯 杯 杯 杯 杯 杯 杯

杯

杯	杯	杯					

瓶 瓶 瓶 瓶 瓶 瓶 瓶 瓶 瓶 瓶

瓶

瓶	瓶	瓶					

罐 罐 罐 罐 罐 罐 罐 罐 罐 罐 罐 罐 罐 罐 罐 罐
罐 罐 罐 罐 罐 罐 罐

罐

罐	罐	罐					

点 | 点点点点点点点点点

点 | 点 | 点 | 点 | | | | |

来 来 来 来 来 来 来

来 | 来 | 来 | 来 | | | | |

再 再 再 再 再 再

再 | 再 | 再 | 再 | | | | |

2. Write what you would like to have for Monday morning breakfast if you have a test at 10 a.m. that day.

_____

_____

_____

3. You plan to invite Karen for dinner. Based on the following ingredients, what questions do you need to ask to decide what to prepare for her?

Ingredients		Questions to ask:
可乐	果汁	_____
牛肉	鸡肉	_____
西瓜	苹果	_____
面条	炒饭	_____
		_____

4. Fill in the blanks using the appropriate measure words in the word bank.

> Ⓐ 碗　Ⓑ 盘　Ⓒ 碟　Ⓓ 份　Ⓔ 块
>
> Ⓕ 杯　Ⓖ 瓶　Ⓗ 罐　Ⓘ 个

1) 三_____蛋糕

2) 五_____可乐

3) 两_____面

4) 六_____披萨

5) 一_____炒饭

6) 四_____春卷

7) 三_____果汁

8) 五_____沙拉

9) 两_____茶

10) 三_____面包

REVIEW 2 (Lessons 6 – 10)

1. Listen to the descriptions and match them to the correct pictures.

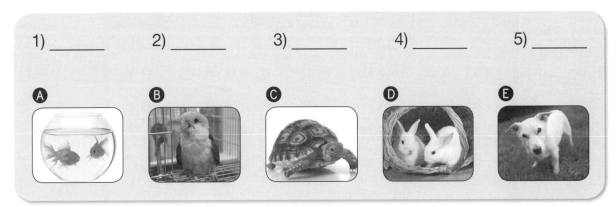

1) _____ 2) _____ 3) _____ 4) _____ 5) _____

Ⓐ Ⓑ Ⓒ Ⓓ Ⓔ

2. Write down what you hear in *pinyin* and match them with the pictures above.

1) _____ Picture (   )   2) _____ Picture (   )

3) _____ Picture (   )   4) _____ Picture (   )

5) _____ Picture (   )

3. Listen to the dialog. Where should Michelle go to find Mike?

Ⓐ

Ⓑ

Ⓒ

Ⓓ

(   )

4. Josh is new to the school and wishes to know where the cafeteria is to have his lunch. Listen to the dialog and tell in which direction he should go.

A 东　　　　　**B** 南　　　　　**C** 西　　　　　**D** 北　　　　　(　)

5. Listen to the recordings and answer the questions based on the class schedule below.

Schedule	星期一	星期二	星期三	星期四	星期五
8:00 – 8.45	英语	电脑	英语	物理	中文
9:00 – 9.45	数学	化学	数学	数学	电脑
10:00 – 10.45	物理	历史	物理	地理	历史
11:00 – 11.45	地理	音乐	电脑	化学	化学
Lunch Break (12:00 – 1:00 pm)					
1:00 – 1.45	电脑	中文	地理	音乐	英语
2:00 – 2.45	体育	体育	体育	体育	

1) **A** 星期一　　**B** 星期二　　**C** 星期三　　**D** 星期四　　(　)

2) **A** 12:00　　**B** 1:45　　**C** 2:45　　**D** 3:45　　(　)

3) **A** 英语　　**B** 化学　　**C** 数学　　**D** 电脑　　(　)

4) **A** 英语　　**B** 地理　　**C** 物理　　**D** 历史　　(　)

5) **A** 星期二　　**B** 星期四　　**C** 星期五　　**D** 星期二、五　　(　)

6) **A** 2节　　**B** 3节　　**C** 4节　　**D** 5节　　(　)

7) **A** 英语　　**B** 地理　　**C** 物理　　**D** 体育　　(　)

8) **A** 电脑　　**B** 地理　　**C** 音乐　　**D** 体育　　(　)

9) **A** 从星期一到星期四　　**B** 从星期一到星期五
　　C 从 2:00 到 2:45　　**D** 从 3:00 到 3:45　　(　)

10) **A** 9节　　**B** 9门　　**C** 29节　　**D** 29门　　(　)

6. Listening rejoinder. Choose the most appropriate response.

1) Ⓐ 她打得很好。　　Ⓑ 她不会打。
Ⓒ 她爱好打网球。　　Ⓓ 她不想打。　　　(　)

2) Ⓐ 他滑得很慢。　　Ⓑ 他会滑雪。
Ⓒ 他不喜欢滑雪。　　Ⓓ 他的爱好是滑雪。　　(　)

3) Ⓐ 打网球。　　Ⓑ 橄榄球打得很好。
Ⓒ 他们不喜欢运动。　　Ⓓ 想当运动员。　　(　)

4) Ⓐ 我不想弹钢琴。　　Ⓑ 我想跳舞。
Ⓒ 我想当歌手。　　Ⓓ 现在我当学生。　　(　)

5) Ⓐ 他天天在书房。　　Ⓑ 他想当作家。
Ⓒ 他将来是作家。　　Ⓓ 他喜欢看书。　　(　)

6) Ⓐ 他每天早上都不学。　　Ⓑ 他昨天学了。
Ⓒ 是的，他每天学。　　Ⓓ 他学过。　　(　)

7. Listen to the descriptions. Match the tastes below to the correct pictures based on what you hear.

Ⓐ　Ⓑ　Ⓒ　Ⓓ

Ⓔ　Ⓕ　Ⓖ　Ⓗ

1) 好吃 _____ 　　2) 好喝 _____

3) 酸 _____ 　　4) 甜 _____

5) 苦 _____ 　　6) 辣 _____

7) 咸 _____ 　　8) 淡 _____

1. Talk about the animals you like and dislike. Use 还, 不, 也, 也不 and 最.

   Example: 我喜欢……，还喜欢……

   我不喜欢……，也不喜欢……

   我最喜欢的动物是……

2. Describe the following pictures using 有.

   Example:

   桌子<u>有</u>一个电脑。

   1)

   2)

   3)

3. Talk about the subjects you have. Follow the example.

   > 我有八门课：中文、数学、英语、历史、地理、物理、音乐和体育。我学过生物，没学过化学。
   >
   > 明天我有四节课：数学、体育、音乐和历史。

4. Imagine that you are asking a new friend about his/her hobbies and dreams. What questions will you ask? What will be his/her reply?

5. Talk about what you want to have for breakfast, lunch and dinner tomorrow. Plan a balanced diet based on the food pyramid guidelines.

6. Imagine that you are going to a Chinese restaurant for dinner. You have to order food in Chinese. Make up a dialog between you and the waiter/waitress.

1. Read the following e-mail and determine whether the sentences below are true (T) or false (F).

小明：

　　你好！

　　今天我要介绍我喜欢的宠物和动物。
　　　　jièshào
　　　　introduce

　　我家有一只小猫，一只大狗，还有两只兔子。小猫是奶奶的宠物，大狗是爷爷的宠物，两只兔子是我的宠物。

　　我最喜欢的宠物是兔子。我也喜欢鱼，不喜欢猫，因为猫吃鱼。
　　　　　　　　　　　　　　　　　　　　　　　　yīnwèi
　　　　　　　　　　　　　　　　　　　　　　　　because

　　我最喜欢的动物是狮子，因为我喜欢电影《狮子王》。我最不喜欢蛇。
　　　　　　　　　　　　　　　　　　　　king

　　你家有什么宠物？你喜欢不喜欢狮子？中国人喜欢什么动物？

　　祝　　快乐！

　　　　　　　　　　　　　　　　　　　　马丁
　　　　　　　　　　　　　　　　　　　　2012年4月6日

1) 马丁家有一只大猫，一只小狗。　　　（　　　）
2) 两只兔子是爷爷的宠物。　　　　　　（　　　）
3) 马丁喜欢猫，也喜欢鱼。　　　　　　（　　　）
4) 美国人最喜欢的动物是狮子。　　　　（　　　）
5) 马丁不知道小明家有没有宠物。　　　（　　　）
6) 马丁知道中国人喜欢什么动物。　　　（　　　）

2. Match the questions in column A to the correct answers in column B.

Column A	Column B
你有几门课？ •	• 不是，是粉红色的。
明天我们有电脑课吗？ •	• 有一个钟和一张地图。
你家离学校远不远？ •	• 没有，星期五有。
你的文具袋是紫色的吗？ •	• 我有七门课。
借我一块橡皮，行吗？ •	• 在操场旁边。
教室的墙上有什么？ •	• 不远。
图书馆在哪儿？ •	• 行，给你。

3. Read the following words or phrases and rearrange them to form sentences.

1) 学校 体育馆 有 里 没有

_____

2) 操场 体育馆 南边 在 的

_____

3) 教室 图书馆 很近 离

_____

4) 桌子 尺子 上 一把 有 白色的

_____

5) 借 圆珠笔 一支 红色的 行吗 我

_____

6) 生物课 我们 有 没 星期三

_____

4. Read the following text and answer the questions.

> 　　现在是下午一点，电脑室里有很多同学。小伟在电脑前打电话，芳芳在他旁边发短信。
>
> 　　下午两点以后，我们还有两节课。今天下午第一节课是美术课，第二节课是体育课。我们四点放学。

1) 小伟和芳芳在哪里上网？

_____

2) 下午几点上课？

_____

3) 下午第二节课是什么课？

_____

4) 今天下午有没有英语课？

_____

5. **Read Xiaowei's blog entry and answer the questions.**

Friday, June 15, 2012

　　八岁以前，我的爱好是打乒乓球、踢足球、跳舞和唱歌。上学以后，我最喜欢唱歌和跳舞。我每星期一、三、五学习唱歌，二、四、六学习跳舞。老师说我唱歌唱得很好，跳舞也跳得很好。我将来想当一个会跳舞的歌手。现在我每天都很忙，也很快乐。

1) 小伟八岁以前的爱好是什么？

_____

2) 他现在的爱好是什么？

_____

3) 他唱歌唱得怎么样？

_____

4) 他跳舞跳得好吗？

_____

5) 他每个星期几学唱歌和跳舞？

_____

6) 小伟将来想当什么？

_____

6. Match the questions in column A to the correct answers in column B.

Column A	Column B
你喝什么？	来两个包子，再来一碗面。
汉堡好吃吗？	我喝中国茶。
可乐好喝吗？	很好吃。
西瓜甜不甜？	我最喜欢吃面条。
你最喜欢吃什么？	很好喝。
你要吃什么？	我吃油条。
你吃饺子还是油条？	我要吃蛋炒饭。
你要点什么菜？	西瓜很甜，很好吃。

7. Mike did a simple class survey on what his classmates would like for lunch today. Read the survey findings and determine whether the sentences below are true (T) or false (F).

今天中午我们班有三个同学要在学校的中国食堂吃午饭。

他们都想吃中国菜。芳芳喜欢吃咸的，她想点一碗面，再点一碟饺子。安琪喜欢吃辣的，她要吃麻婆豆腐，喝酸辣汤。玛丽喜欢吃甜的，她想来一份糖醋排骨，再来一杯甜豆浆。

1) Four students want to have Chinese food for lunch. (   )

2) Fangfang likes spicy food.   (   )

3) *Jiaozi* is a kind of savory food.   (   )

4) Anqi likes sour food.   (   )

5) *Mapo Doufu* is bitter.   (   )

6) *Tangcu Paigu* has a sweet taste.   (   )

1. Write an e-mail to your Chinese friend introducing the pets in your family (if you don't have any, make one up), and say what animals you like and dislike.

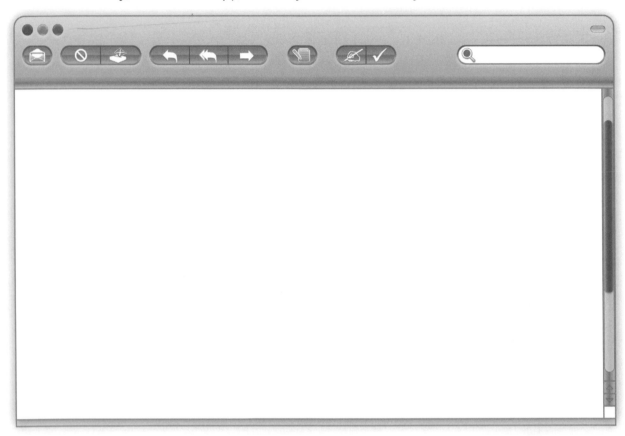

2. You found a bag in the library this morning. Based on the items shown here, fill in the description form in Chinese. This form will be placed on the Lost and Found board to provide the necessary information for the owner to identify and retrieve his or her lost items.

Item(s): _____

Place found: _____

Time found: _____

Contact details: _____

3.   Form Chinese words that end with the following characters.

1) 室： _____

2) 馆： _____

3) 厅： _____

4) 房： _____

4.   Answer the following questions in Chinese.

1) 你有几门课？今天有几节课？

_____

2) 明天从九点到十点你有什么课？

_____

3) 你一个星期有几节中文课？

_____

4) 你几点上课？几点放学？

_____

5) 昨天晚上你上网了吗？

_____

6) 星期六你做什么了？

_____

5.   Compose a paragraph to introduce your interests and dreams. Write at least five sentences stating your interests, how good you are at then, how frequently you engage in each of them each week, and what you want to be in the future.

_____

_____

_____

_____

191

6. Your Chinese friend, Fangfang, is coming to your house this Saturday for lunch. You want to prepare something that is different from what she normally eats. Come up with a simple menu in Chinese that consists of a soup, a main course, a drink, and a dessert.

汤： _____

主食： _____

饮料： _____

甜品： _____

7. Your cousin is going to work as a part-time waiter in a Chinese restaurant. He is worried that he may not be able to take orders from customers. Make a dialog on food ordering in Chinese to show him the common phrases and expressions he will need to use.